Folk Songs of
England, Ireland, Scotland
and Wales

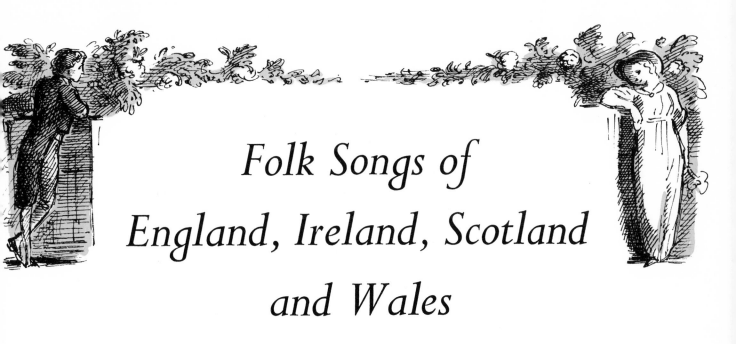

Folk Songs of
England, Ireland, Scotland
and Wales

SELECTED AND EDITED BY

William Cole

ARRANGED FOR PIANO AND GUITAR BY

NORMAN MONATH

DRAWINGS BY EDWARD ARDIZZONE

DOUBLEDAY & COMPANY, INC.

GARDEN CITY, NEW YORK,

1961

Special acknowledgment is made to the following, who have granted permission for the use of the material listed below:

"An Eriskay Love Lilt from *Songs of the Hebrides,* Vol. I." Copyright 1909 by Boosey & Co. Ltd., Renewed 1936. Renewal assigned to Boosey & Hawkes, Inc. Reprinted by permission.

"Road to the Isles" and "Weaving Lilt from *Songs of the Hebrides,* Vol. II." Copyright 1917 by Boosey & Co. Ltd., Renewed 1944. Renewal assigned to Boosey & Hawkes, Inc. Reprinted by permission.

"She Moved through the Fair." Lyrics by Padraic Colum.

"John O'Dwyer of the Glen." Lyrics by Frank O'Connor.

Contents

England

Ireland

Scotland

Wales

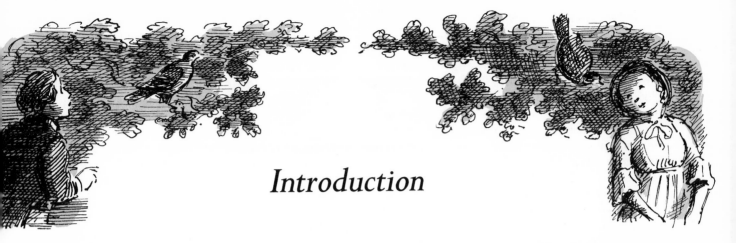

Introduction

It is an act of temerity to bring forth a new book in a field so full of spiky scholars and overnight experts as is the booming world of folk song. It is a world full of variety and contrast. On one hand are the pure traditionalists and the academic folklorists who bristle if anyone changes so much as one note or one word in any song, even though the songs in their original form may be virtually unsingable. At the other extreme—far, far at the other extreme—are the boys from Tin Pan Alley who are out for a quick dollar. They overarrange lovely traditional songs, copyright them in their own names, and inflict them on the rest of us through the medium of male trios with a jazz beat.

This book is not for the scholars (although it couldn't have come about without them), and it certainly isn't for the commercializers. I like to think it is for the many hundreds of degrees of folk song *aficionados* in between. These songs from the British Isles have always seemed to me the most beautiful songs in the world. They are shot through with the poetry of the people; they celebrate love and nature, the flair of the hero and the pride of the simple man. They are sometimes killingly humorous, sometimes jaunty or unashamedly amorous. Each song grew out of a deep feeling one man once had. His expression in song was intensely personal and yet universal enough that the men around him picked up his song and passed it on. And the next generation passed it on again, and the next again, until it became an unself-conscious heritage.

There must be a hundred different definitions of "folk song." Defining folk song is like defining humor; somebody is always making a try at it. I am told that an early edition of the Encyclopaedia Britannica defined a folk song as "the uncouth vocal utterance of the people." These fighting words were considerably modified in later editions. The official definition of the International Folk Music Council has a forbiddingly academic ring to it: "Music that

has submitted to the process of oral transmission: it is the product of evolution and is dependent on the circumstances of continuity, variation, and selection." This kind of talk is certainly a long way from a Welsh country pub or a Scotch croft. But in its unfolklike way, it's a good description. Pete Seeger is much more forthright: "They're called folk songs because folks sing 'em."

The ethnic purists will probably object to the inclusion of some songs in this collection. They seem to feel that if we know who wrote either the words or the music, the song immediately stops being a folk song. For example, Irish folklorists look with a jaundiced eye on the songs of Thomas Moore. Part of this feeling is nationalistic: Moore did not pull his oar properly in the Irish revolutionary movements of his time. He was off in England chumming it up with the Sassenach. The lyrics he wrote to traditional airs do not have the true folk feeling—they're too "literary"— but they were picked up by the folk and have been sung by them ever since. A number of other songs would seem to have had their origin on either the concert stage or the music hall, but they expressed something that people wanted expressed, and they've had staying power. By any liberal definition, they're folk songs now.

While some of these Welsh and Irish songs were picked up during World War II on my own mental tape recorder, I have never been a collector as such. I have never trod out to the hills carrying recording equipment, nor have I uncovered any aged musical manuscripts in the British Museum. The songs in this collection have come from twenty years of enthusiasm; they've come from friends who are folk singers, from folk song concerts, from books, from radio, and from a record collection built up over many years. The comments that appear with each song are a combination of personal opinion and much research in the work of the folk song scholars. The references in the English and Scotch sections to "Child" number so-and-so refer to James Francis Child, who was, oddly enough, an American, and who was also the man most responsible for the orderly preservation of the great English and Scotch songs. This Harvard professor (1825–96) collected, edited, and numbered 305 *English and Scottish Popular Ballads,* and his work has been the cornerstone of folk song scholarship ever since. The other great collector and preserver referred to from time to time was Cecil Sharp, an Englishman who collected and wrote voluminously, and who spent some time in the Appalachian mountains, where he discovered to his surprise that many English and Scotch songs were preserved *there* in a purer form than in their home country.

The first basic collection of Irish traditional airs was gathered at the end of the eighteenth century by an Englishman, Edward Bunting. Subsequent scholars whose books have been treasure troves were Dr. George Petrie and P. W. Joyce. Two contemporary books that are commendable indeed are *Irish Street Ballads* by Colm O'Lochlainn and "Songs of the Irish" by Donal O'Sullivan. Most of the Scotch songs stem from the basic collections: *Playford's "Choice Ayres,"* (seventeenth century) and two eighteenth-century collections, *Johnson's "Scots Musical Museum"* and *Oswald's "Companion."* The books and records of the great contemporary Scotch singer Ewan MacColl are invaluable to any anthologist, and there is an exciting three-volume collection, *Songs of the Hebrides,* by Majory Kennedy-Fraser and Kenneth MacLeod that is a delight.

The finest collection of Welsh folk songs is *The National Songs of Wales,* a revised edition of a book originally compiled by Brinley Richards in 1873 and brought up to date last year by E. T. Davies and Sydney Northcote.

It is fascinating, going through the world of folk music, to find out what nice-nellies many of the early collectors were. Folk song, stemming from the people, tends to be earthy; spades are called spades, and in a perfectly natural way. But the nineteenth-century scholars were horrified and went into a frenzy of emendation. I have tried my best to restore these songs to their original pleasantly vulgar state, and have had much help from two fine books by James Reeves, *The Idiom of the People* and *The Everlasting Circle.* It was interesting to find that, for bawdry, the English lead the field. Then come the Scotch, led by Robert Burns in his more unbuttoned moments. There is almost nothing about sex in the Irish and Welsh folk song; or at least, the songs that aren't snow white haven't had much circulation.

Welsh folk songs are all but unknown in the United States. They are not in the repertoire of any of the popular folk singers, and only three of them, "All Through the Night," "The Ash Grove," and "Men of Harlech," are known here. The Welsh are the loveliest and most varied songs of all, but the difficulties of the language are staggering to contemplate, and the translations heretofore available were lamentably stilted and Victorian. It was only after much pondering that I decided to print the Welsh songs in both English and a kind of do-it-yourself Welsh phonetics. I decided on phonetics instead of Welsh itself after contemplating how an American would get his tongue around—to take an example at random—the first lines of "Rise, Rise Thou Merry Lark":

> Clyw! clyw! foreuol glod,
> O! fwyned yw'r defn yn nau'n dod,
> O wynfa lan i lawr.

The phonetics I've worked up are similar to those I used for myself when I was writing down songs in Wales during the war. I have sung them back to many Welshmen, who understood every word, but remarked that they came through with a strange, undefinable accent. I must say that I was baffled for a while in my home-grown phonetics about the proper way to approach the two Welsh sounds that aren't in English: the "ch" and the double l. (I've pointed these sounds up in the text by putting them in italics.) If the footnote explaining the double l doesn't quite give the picture, let me cite how two Welsh authorities explain the sound: one says "put the tip of the tongue against the roof of the mouth and hiss," and the other "put the tip of your tongue immediately above your teeth and breathe." It's really not difficult.

I want to thank those who knowingly helped me during the making of this book, and those who unknowingly did so. Among the latter are the folk singers I have listened to, the compilers of many other books, and the artists whose records are listed in the Discography—especially Alan Lomax, whose three records of England, Scotch, and Irish songs in his Columbia World Library of Folk and Primitive Music are but one small portion of his immense contribution to folk music. My first thanks are to my collaborator, Norman Monath, who was amazingly patient with a musical semi-literate, and who worked the songs over and over again until each was just right. And my gratitude and affection to Pyke Johnson, Jr., of Doubleday who started this whole thing, and who, as my editor, must have had moments when he wished he hadn't. Gramercy, gramercy to Diana Klemin and Denise Rathbun of Doubleday who nagged me in the nicest possible way to produce a little faster; to Oscar Brand, my old friend, who cast an expert eye on the Table of Contents early in the game; to Peggy Bennett Cole, who helped discover many of the songs; to Patrick Clancy of the Clancy

Brothers, who cleared up some fine points; to Charlotte Day of the English-Speaking Union, to Moses Asch of Folkways Records, to Frank O'Connor, who helped me with the Irish phonetics and who, I *think*, approved of more of the Irish songs than he disapproved. Welsh scholars are not in abundance in New York City, and my greatest good fortune was to meet Peter John Stephens, a poet and playwright, who devoted hour upon hour to the dull business of Welsh phonetics, and whose new translations of many of the Welsh songs, done especially for this volume, will surely become the standard ones. I bow to him deeply.

WILLIAM COLE

A Note On The Arrangements

There is no limit to the number of different ways any one folk song can be arranged. Nor is there any one way that a folk song *ought* to be arranged, any more than there is any one way that a rose ought to be shaped to be beautiful.

My aim here is to present simple, straightforward, and universally identifiable arrangements, as opposed to those that are highly stylized and ornate, or reflect the personal voice of the arranger. The latter have their place, and are effective, when undertaken by a composer like Benjamin Britten who has given us some extremely beautiful arrangements of British folk songs, all of which bear the stamp of his individual creativity and often evoke moods not hitherto associated with a particular song.

But this is a book for people who want simple arrangements sufficiently adaptable to be played the way *they* want to play them. Therefore, these arrangements are not inherently committed to any particular tempo, mood, or level of expression. Of course, a lullaby cannot be arranged so that it will be playable as a march. Such extremes aside, these arrangements comfortably allow for a wide range of variation in performance. By using simple left-hand accompaniments and orthodox harmonies, and by allowing the melody to sing out in the right-hand part, the basic elements of the song are simply and directly provided. Most of the expressive markings and tempo indications were suggested by my collaborator, William Cole, and they should be taken as suggestions rather than dogma. Surely if artists can differ in their interpretations of a Chopin prelude, who is to say that a given folk song should be played andante rather than moderato? As a matter of fact, why play a song the same way each time?

To be sure, folk songs have their traditions which no arranger should capriciously ignore, and for that reason, all the songs in this book were carefully researched. However, in making use of these arrangements, the performer should give full freedom to his own expressive instincts, making any musical changes he desires. In that way new traditions will replace the old, in keeping with the spirit and meaning of folk music.

NORMAN MONATH

The Songs of England

Hares on the Mountains

A popular song found in many versions by Cecil Sharp and other folk-song collectors in the west of England. It should be sung slowly, with great feeling. It expresses the sweetly remembered joys of pursuit better than any other song in the language.

Moderato

Young wo-men, they run like hares on the moun-tain; Young wo-men they run ___ like hares on the moun-tain, If I were but a young man I'd soon go a-hunt-ing, To my

molto rit.   affrettando

right fol - did-dle - de - ro, To my right fol - did-dle - dee.

a tempo *poco rit. e dim.*

Young women, they run like hares on the mountain,
Young women, they run like hares on the mountain,
If I were but a young man I'd soon go a-hunting,
To my right fol-diddle-de-ro,
To my right fol-diddle-dee.

Young women they sing like birds in the bushes,
Young women they sing like birds in the bushes,
If I were but a young man I'd go bang them bushes,
To my right fol-diddle-de-ro,
To my right fol-diddle-dee.

Young women they swim like ducks in the water,
Young women they swim like ducks in the water,
If I were but a young man I soon would swim after,
To my right fol-diddle-de-ro,
To my right fol-diddle-dee.

Young women they bloom like laurel in springtime,
Young women they bloom like laurel in springtime,
If I were but a young man I'd soon go and pluck some,
To my right fol-diddle-de ro,
To my right fol-diddle-dee.

Young women they run like hares on the mountain,
Young women they run like hares on the mountain,
If I were but a young man I soon would run after,
To my right fol-diddle-de-ro,
To my right fol-diddle-dee.

3

Allan Water

MONK LEWIS

A composed song, rather than a pure folk song, much favored by tenors, on the time-honored theme of man's inhumanity to woman.

Andante

On the banks of Al-lan wa - ter, When the sweet spring-time did fall, — Was the mil - ler's love-ly daugh-ter, Fair-est of them all. For his bride a sol-dier sought her, And a win - ning tongue had

he, ___ On the banks of Al lan wa-ter, None so gay as she.

On the banks of Allan water,
   When the sweet springtime did fall,
Was the miller's lovely daughter,
   Fairest of them all.
For his bride a soldier sought her,
   And a winning tongue had he,
On the banks of Allan water,
   None so gay as she.

On the banks of Allan water,
   When brown autumn spread its store,
There I saw the miller's daughter,
   But she smiled no more.
For the summer, grief had brought her,
   And the soldier false was he;
On the banks of Allan water,
   None so sad as she!

On the banks of Allan water,
   When the winter snow fell fast,
Still was seen the miller's daughter,
   Chilling blew the blast.
But the miller's lovely daughter,
   Both from cold and care was free;
On the banks of Allan water,
   There a corpse lay she!

5

My Boy Willie

Two great folk-song collectors were at odds about the origin of this jaunty song; Sabine Baring-Gould regarded it as a forerunner of the famous "Lord Randal." On the other hand, Cecil Sharp claimed that was a comic derivative, or burlesque, of Randal. Another version, "Oh where have you been, Billy Boy, Billy Boy," is more familiar in America.

Animato

O, where have you been all the day, My boy Wil-lie?— O,

where have you been all the day, Wil-lie, won't you tell me now?

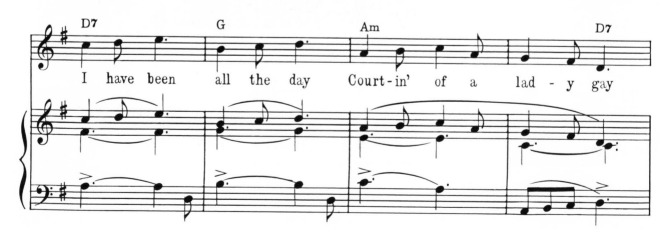

I have been all the day Court-in' of a lad-y gay

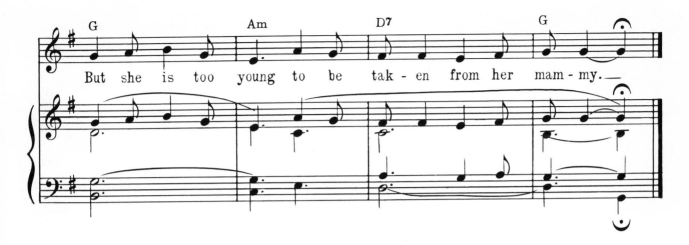

But she is too young to be tak-en from her mam-my.

O, where have you been all the day,
  My boy Willie?
O, where have you been all the day,
  Willie, won't you tell me now?
I have been all the day
  Courtin' of a lady gay
But she is too young to be taken from her
  mammy.

O, can she bake and can she brew,
  My boy Willie?
O, can she bake and can she brew,
  Willie, won't you tell me now?
She can brew, she can bake,
  She can make a weddin' cake
But she is too young to be taken from her
  mammy.

O, can she make up a bed, *etc.*
She can make up a bed
  Fifty feet above her head, *etc.*

O, can she cook a plate of fish, *etc.*
She can cook a plate of fish
  With her fingers in the dish, *etc.*

O, can she sew and can she spin, *etc.*
She can sew and she can spin,
  She can do most anythin' *etc.*

O, how old can she be, *etc.*
She is two, she is seven,
  She is twenty-and-eleven, *etc.*

O, did you ask her to wed, *etc.*
Yes, I asked her to wed,
  And these are the words she said:
"I am much too young to be taken from my
  mammy."

When Cockleshells Turn Silverbells

This appears to be an English mutation of the Scottish "O Waly, Waly," which is itself obscure in its origins, but is placed roughly early in the seventeenth century. "Waly, waly" *may* come from Shakespeare's "Willow, willow." It should be sung slowly, with much feeling.

Andante con molto espress.

When cock - le shells _____ turn sil - ver - bells, _____ And mus-sels

grow _____ on ev'ry tree. _____ When blooms the

rose _____ 'mongst frost and snows, _____ Then will my

false _____ love prove true to me. _____

Meno mosso

O wa - ly, wa - ly, but love is bon - nie, A lit - tle

while _____ when it is new. _____ But when it's

old _____ it grow - eth cold, _____ And fades a -

rit. e dim.

a tempo

doloroso

9

way——————— like morn-ing dew——————

grazioso

rit. e dim.

When cockleshells turn silverbells,
And mussels grow on every tree.
When blooms the rose 'mongst frost and
    snows,
Then will my false love prove true to me.

O waly, waly, but love is bonnie,
A little while when it is new.
But when it's old, it groweth cold,
And fades away like morning dew.

O had I wist before I kissed,
That love had been so ill to win;
I'd locked my heart in case of gold
And pinned it with a silver pin.

O waly, waly, but love is bonnie,
A little while when it is new.
But when it's old, it groweth cold,
And fades away like morning dew.

The Banks of the Sweet Primroses

A song reported by Cecil Sharp and other collectors in Devon, Sussex, Hampshire, Somerset, and just about every other part of England. The collectors have noted that, wherever found, the tune and the words show a surprising consistency; there is something about the lyrics that kept them almost intact when passing on from person to person. This is easy to believe; who could ever lose lines such as "Where the pretty little small birds/Do change their voices . . ."?

Oh, as I walked out one mid-sum-mer's morn-ing, For to view the fields and the flow-ers so gay, 'Twas there on the banks of the sweet prim-ros-es That I be-

held— a most pleas-ant maid. 'Twas there— on the

banks of the sweet prim - ros - es That I— be-

held— a most pleas - ant maid.

rit. *smorzato*

Oh, as I walked out one midsummer's
    morning,
For to view the fields and the flowers so gay,
'Twas there on the banks of the sweet
    primroses
That I beheld a most pleasant maid.
'Twas there on the banks of the sweet
    primroses
That I beheld a most pleasant maid.

Are you sad, fair maid, what makes you
    wander,
What is the cause of all your grief?
I will make you as happy as any lady,
If you will grant me one small relief.
I will make you as happy as any lady,
If you will grant me one small relief.

Stand off, young man, and don't be so
    deceitful,
'Tis you that are the cause of all my pain,
It is you that has caused my poor heart to
    wander,
And to find comfort it's all in vain.
It is you that has caused my poor heart to
    wander,
And to find comfort it's all in vain.

I will go down to some lonely valley,
Where no man on earth there shall me find,
Where the pretty little small birds do change
    their voices,
And every moment blows blusterous wind.
Where the pretty little small birds do change
    their voices,
And every moment blows blusterous wind.

So come all fair maids, by me take a warning,
And pay attention to what I say,
There is many a dark and a cloudy morning
Turns out a bright and sunshiny day.
There is many a dark and a cloudy morning
Turns out a bright and sunshiny day.

13

I'm Seventeen Come Sunday

There are many variations of this rural song. One, rewritten by Robert Burns, appeared in *Scots Musical Museum* in 1792. James Reeves has written, "The original of this song, whatever it was, shocked all the editors, from the eighteenth century onwards, into a frenzy of emendation. . . ." This version is partially restored. In the phrase, "And a merry man in the morning," this particular usage of "merry" means "amorously inclined, willing."

As I walked out one May morn-ing, One_ May morn-ing so

ear-ly, I ov-er-took a hand-some maid _____ Just

as the sun was ris-ing With my rue dum day, fol the did-dle dol

Fol the dol the did-dle dum the day.

poco rit. e dim.   *smorzato*

As I walked out one May morning,
One May morning so early,
I overtook a handsome maid
Just as the sun was rising.
> *With my rue dum day, fol the diddle dol*
> *Fol the dol the diddle dum the day.*

Her shoes were bright, her stockings white,
And her buckles shone like silver;
She had a black and a roving eye
And her hair hung down her shoulder.
> *With my rue dum day, fol the diddle dol*
> *Fol the dol the diddle dum the day.*

How old are you my fair pretty maid?
How old are you my honey?
She answered me right cheerfully,
I'm seventeen come Sunday.
> *With my rue dum day, fol the diddle dol*
> *Fol the dol the diddle dum the day.*

Can you love me, my fair pretty maid?
Will you marry me, my honey?
She answered me quite cheerfully,
I dare not for my Mummy.
> *With my rue dum day, fol the diddle dol*
> *Fol the dol the diddle dum the day.*

If you'll come to my Mummy's house
When the moon is shining clearly,
I will come down and let you in,
And my Mummy shall not hear me.
> *With my rue dum day, fol the diddle dol*
> *Fol the dol the diddle dum the day.*

I went down to her Mummy's house
When the moon was brightly shining;
She did come down and let me in,
And we lay with our arms entwining.
> *With my rue dum day, fol the diddle dol*
> *Fol the dol the diddle dum the day.*

Now soldier will you marry me?
Now is your time or never;
For if you do not marry me,
I am undone for ever.
> *With my rue dum day, fol the diddle dol*
> *Fol the dol the diddle dum the day.*

And now she is the soldier's wife,
And the soldier loves her dearly;
The drum and fife is her delight,
And a merry man in the morning.
> *With my rue dum day, fol the diddle dol*
> *Fol the dol the diddle dum the day.*

Greensleeves

No folk song in the world is as indestructible as this one, and none has been subjected to more indignities. It has been played on electric guitars and sung by female quartets. It has been used as an advertising jingle and twisted by vulgar parodies. But it still holds and haunts. The earliest written reference to it was in 1580. A reading of the lyrics will show that it is not a sweet, innocuous love song, but a plea from a sixteenth-century sugar daddy to his bored mistress. There are many versions of the lyrics; perhaps the next best-known is "A Happy New Year."

Andante

A - las, my love, you do me wrong To cast me off _ dis - court-eous-ly; And

I have lov - éd you so long,— De - light - ing in _ your com - pa - ny.

Green - sleeves was all my joy,— Green - sleeves was my de - light;

Green-sleeves was my heart of gold, And who but my la - dy Green-sleeves?

Alas, my Love! ye do me wrong
　To cast me off discourteously;
And I have lovéd you so long,
　Delighting in your company.

Greensleeves was all my joy,
　Greensleeves was my delight;
Greensleeves was my heart of gold,
　And who but my Lady Greensleeves?

I have been ready at your hand,
　To grant whatever you would crave;
I have both wagéd life and land,
　Your love and goodwill for to have.
Chorus:

I bought thee kerchers to thy head,
　That were wrought fine and gallantly;
I kept thee both at board and bed,
　Which cost my purse well favouredly.
Chorus:

I bought thee petticoats of the best,
　The cloth so fine as fine might be;
I gave thee jewels for thy chest,
　And all this cost I spent on thee.
Chorus:

Thy purse and eke thy agy* gilt knives,
　Thy pincase gallant to the eye;
No better wore the burgess wives,
　And yet thou wouldst not love me.
Chorus:

Thy gown was of the grassy green,
　Thy sleeves of satin hanging by,
Which made thee be our harvest queen,
　And yet thou wouldst not love me.
Chorus:

My gayest gelding I thee gave,
　To ride wherever likèd thee;
No lady ever was so brave,
　And yet thou wouldst not love me.
Chorus:

My men were clothèd all in green,
　And they did ever wait on thee;
All this was gallant to be seen,
　And yet thou wouldst not love me.
Chorus:

For every morning when thou rose,
　I sent thee dainties orderly,
To cheer thy stomach from all woes,
　And yet thou wouldst not love me.
Chorus:

Well, I will pray to God on high,
　That thou my constancy mayst see,
And that yet once before I die,
　Thou wilt vouchsafe to love me.
Chorus:

Greensleeves, now farewell! adieu!
　God I pray to prosper thee;
For I am still thy lover true.
　Come once again and love me.
Chorus:

* *agy,* aged, old.

17

The Trees Are Getting High

This beautiful song is found in a multitude of versions all over the British Isles. In England it is also known as "Still Growing." In Scotland it is "Lang A-growing," and in Ireland "The Bonny Boy." It has been traced to a Scotch origin and first appeared in print in *Scots Musical Museum* in 1792. The original song is believed to have been based on an actual case of a child marriage. Such marriages for material reasons were common in the Middle Ages and after. The boy's age is given variously as twelve, thirteen, and sixteen. In one version there is a revelatory stanza: "Twas on one summer morning at the dawning of the day,/ They went into some cornfield to have some sport and play;/ And what they did there she never will declare,/ But she never more complained of his growing."

Andante

The trees are get-ting high,_ and the leaves are grow-ing green, The time has gone and past my love that you and I have seen; 'Twas

18

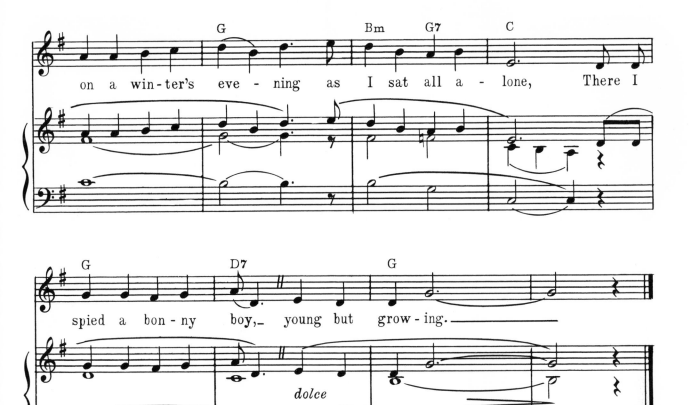

on a win-ter's eve-ning as I sat all a-lone, There I spied a bon-ny boy,— young but grow-ing.——

The trees are getting high, and the leaves are
   growing green,
The time has gone and past my love that you
   and I have seen;
'Twas on a winter's evening as I sat all alone,
There I spied a bonny boy, young but
   growing.

It's mother, dear mother, you've done to me
   much wrong,
You've married me to a bonny boy, his age it
   is so young;
His age is only twelve, myself scarcely
   thirteen,
Saying your bonny boy is young but he's
   growing.

It's daughter, dear daughter I've done to ye no
   wrong,
I've married ye to a bonny boy, he is some
   rich lord's son;
A lady he will make you, if a lady you'll be
   made,
Saying your bonny boy is young but he's
   growing.

It's mother, dear mother, and if it pleases you,
We'll send him to the college for another year
   or two;
And all around his arm we'll tie a ribbon blue,
And that will be a token that he's married.

At the age of thirteen he was a married man,
And at the age of fourteen the father of a son,
And at the age of fifteen his grave was grow-
   ing green,
And that put an end to his growing.

On Ilkley Moor Baht 'At

A song in Yorkshire dialect about a young man who unfortunately crossed Ilkla Moor without his hat. Originally a hymn tune, this is a great one for group singing.

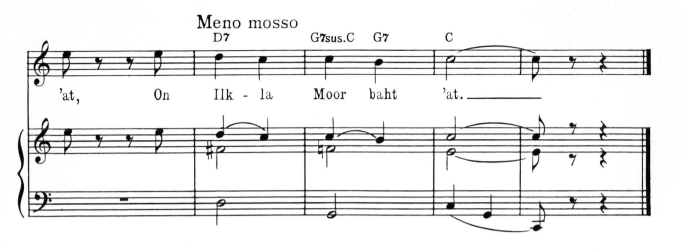

Whear 'as tha' been sin' ah saw thee?
On Ilkla Moor baht 'at,
Whear 'as tha' been sin' ah saw thee?
Whear 'as tha' been sin' ah saw thee?
On Ilkla Moor baht 'at,
On Ilkla Moor baht 'at,
On Ilkla Moor baht 'at.

Tha's been a-coortin' Mary Jayun,
On Ilkla Moor baht 'at,
On Ilkla Moor baht 'at,
On Ilkla Moor baht 'at.

Tha'll go an' get thee death o' cowld,
On Ilkla Moor baht 'at,
On Ilkla Moor baht 'at,
On Ilkla Moor baht 'at.

Then we shall ha' to bury thee,
On Ilkla Moor baht 'at,
On Ilkla Moor baht 'at,
On Ilkla Moor baht 'at.

Then t'worms'll cum an' et thee oop,
On Ilkla Moor baht 'at,
On Ilkla Moor baht 'at,
On Ilkla Moor baht 'at.

Then t'doox'll cum an' et oop t'worms,
On Ilkla Moor baht 'at,
On Ilkla Moor baht 'at,
On Ilkla Moor baht 'at.

Then us'll cum an' et oop t'doox.
On Ilkla Moor baht 'at,
On Ilkla Moor baht 'at,
On Ilkla Moor baht 'at.

Then us'll all 'av etten thee,
On Ilkla Moor baht 'at.
On Ilkla Moor baht 'at,
On Ilkla Moor baht 'at,

That's whear we'll get our owen back,
On Ilkla Moor baht 'at,
On Ilkla Moor baht 'at,
On Ilkla Moor baht 'at.

O Waly, Waly

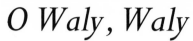

Cecil Sharp reports that he has collected this song in five variants, and lines and phrases from it appear in many other songs in England and America (see "When Cockleshells" in this collection).

Andante sostenuto

The wa - ter is wide, I can - not get o'er
And nei - ther have I wings to fly.
O go and get me some lit - tle boat

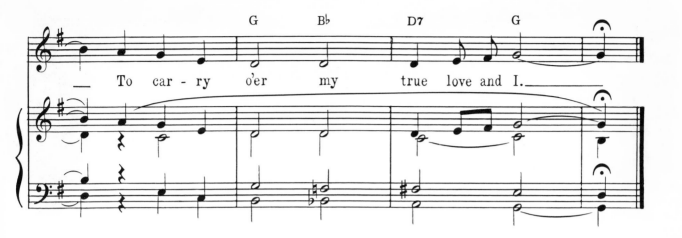

To car-ry o'er my true love and I.

The water is wide, I cannot get o'er
And neither have I wings to fly.
O go and get me some little boat
To carry o'er my true love and I.

Down in the meadows the other day,
A-gath'ring flowr's both fine and gay,
A-gath'ring flowr's both red and blue,
I little thought what love could do.

I put my hand into one soft bush,
Thinking the sweetest flow'r to find.
I prick'd my finger to the bone,
And left the sweetest flow'r alone.

I lean'd my back up against some oak,
Thinking it was a trusty tree.
But first he bended and then he broke,
So did my love prove false to me.

Where love is planted, O there it grows,
It buds and blossoms like some rose;
It has a sweet and pleasant smell,
No flow'r on earth can it excel.

Must I be bound, O, and he go free,
Must I love one that don't love me!
Why should I act such a childish part,
And love a man that will break my heart.

There is a ship sailing on the sea,
She's loaded deep as deep can be,
But not so deep as in love I am;
I care not if I sink or swim.

O love is handsome and love is fine,
And love is charming when it is true;
As it grows older it groweth colder
And fades away like the morning dew.

Weel May the Keel Row

Known also as "As I Came Thro' Sandgate," this song has been claimed by both the Scottish and the English. It is sometimes referred to as the national anthem of the Tyne River (just below the Scottish border). In Tyneside dialect, a "keel" is a boat. The "keelmen" wore blue bonnets. The song first appeared in print in about 1770.

Moderato

As I came thro' Sand-gate, Thro' Sand-gate, thro' Sand-gate, As

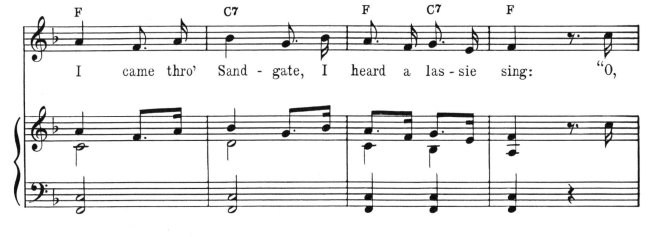

I came thro' Sand-gate, I heard a las-sie sing: "0,

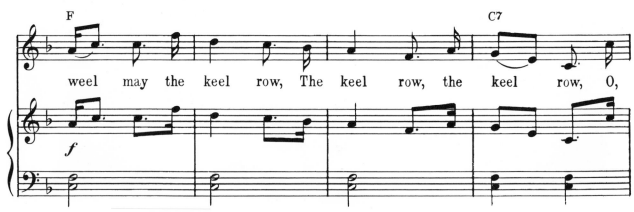

weel may the keel row, The keel row, the keel row, 0,

weel may the keel row That my lad-die's in."

As I came thro' Sandgate,
  Thro' Sandgate, thro' Sandgate,
As I came thro' Sandgate,
  I heard a lassie sing:
"O, weel may the keel row,
  The keel row, the keel row,
O, weel may the keel row
  That my laddie's in.

"O, wha's like my Johnnie,
  Sae leish,* sae blithe, sae bonnie?
He's foremost 'mang the mony
  Keel lads o' coaly Tyne:
He'll set or row sae tightly,
  Or, in the dance sae sprightly,
He'll cut and shuffle sightly,
  'Tis true, were he not mine.

"He wears a blue bonnet,
  Blue bonnet, blue bonnet;
He wears a blue bonnet,
  A dimple in his chin;
And weel may the keel row,
  The keel row, the keel row,
And weel may the keel row,
  That my laddie's in."

* *leish:* lithe.

25

The Three Ravens

One of the ballads collected by Francis James Child (#26), this haunting song dates back to at least 1611. It is also known as "The Twa Corbies." There is a jocular version of it which begins, "There were three crows sat on a tree,/ O Billy McGee, McGaw." "Leman" is an archaic word meaning "sweetheart or mistress." Any doubts about whether the pronunciation, in the first line, should be "ravens" or "ra'ens" will be cleared up by listening to Richard Dyer-Bennett's rendition of the song.

There were three ra'ens sat on a tree, Down a down, hey down, hey down, They were as black as black might be, With a down. The one of them said to his mate, "Where shall we our

break - fast take?" With a down, der - ry, der - ry, der - ry down, down.

allargando

There were three ra'ens sat on a tree,
    Down a down, hey down, hey down,
They were as black as black might be,
    With a down.
The one of them said to his mate,
  "Where shall we our breakfast take?"
With a down, derry, derry, derry down, down.

"Down in yonder green field,
    Down, a down, hey down, hey down,
There lies a knight slain 'neath his shield,
    With a down.
His hounds they lie down at his feet,
So well they do their master keep,
    With a down, derry, derry, derry down, down.

His hawks they fly so eagerly,
No other fowl dare come him nigh,
Down there comes a fallow doe,
As great with young as she might go,

She lifted up his bloody head,
And kissed his wounds that were so red,
She got him up upon her back,
And carried him to earthen lake,

She buried him before the prime,
She was dead herself ere e'en-song time,
God send every gentleman,
Such hawks, such hounds, and such a leman.

Early One Morning

The perfidy of man again. This beautiful song is usually given in truncated form; in this version the poor maiden elaborates on the cause of her troubles.

Moderato

Ear - ly one morn - ing, just as the sun was ris - ing, I

heard a young maid sing _ in the val - ley be - low.

"Oh, don't de - ceive _ me, oh nev - er leave _ me,

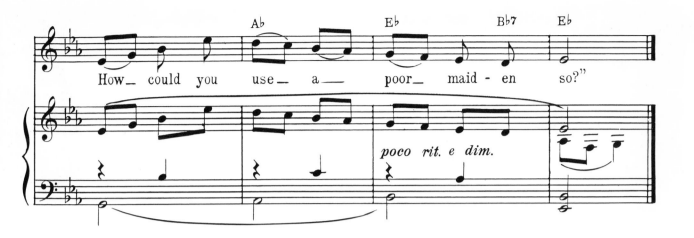

How_ could you use_ a_ poor_ maid - en so?"

poco rit. e dim.

Early one morning, just as the sun was
   rising,
I heard a young maid sing in the valley below.
"Oh don't deceive me, oh never leave me,
How could you use a poor maiden so?

Remember the vows that you made to me
   truly,
Remember how tenderly you nestled close to
   me.
Gay is the garland, fresh are the roses
I've culled from the garden to bind over thee.

Here I now wander alone as I wonder
Why did you leave me to sigh and complain.
I ask of the roses, why should I be forsaken,
Why must I here in sorrow remain?

Through yonder grove, by the spring that is
   running,
There you and I have so merrily played,
Kissing and courting and gently sporting,
Oh, my innocent heart you've betrayed.

How could you slight so a pretty girl who
   loves you,
A pretty girl who loves you so dearly and
   warm?
Though love's folly is surely but a fancy,
Still it should prove to me sweeter than your
   scorn.

Soon you will meet with another pretty
   maiden,
Some pretty maiden, you'll court her for a
   while;
Thus ever ranging, turning and changing,
Always seeking for a girl that is new."

Thus sang the maiden, her sorrows be-
   wailing,
Thus sang the maid in the valley below:
"Oh don't deceive me, oh never leave me,
How could you use a poor maiden so?"

O No, John!

There are a dizzying number of variations of this charming song. The version most frequently heard has suffered from bowdlerization by Cecil Sharp: ". . . the lines were coarse and needed considerable revision." It is believed to have stemmed from old English "singing games," and is a close relative of such songs as "The Keys to Canterbury." It is amusing to consider that there is a Salvation Army version entitled "Yes, Lord!" A fascinating discussion of the song may be found in James Reeves' *The Idiom of the People.*

Allegretto

On yon-der hill there stands a— crea-ture; Who she is I

do not know. I'll go and court her for her— beau - ty,

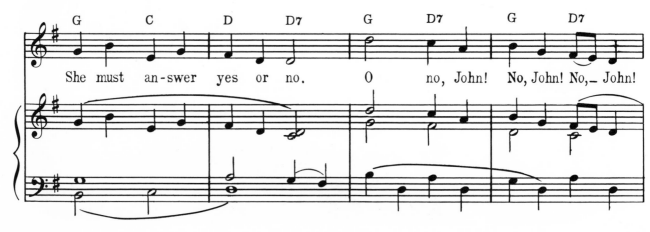

She must an-swer yes or no. O no, John! No, John! No,— John!

Five times
Sixth time

No!   2. My   No!

On yonder hill there stands a creature;
Who she is I do not know.
I'll go and court her for her beauty,
She must answer yes or no.
    O no, John! No, John! No, John! No!

On her bosom are bunches of posies,
On her breast where flowers grow;
If I should chance to touch that posy,
She must answer yes or no.
    O no, John! No, John! No, John! No!

Madam I am come for to court you,
If your favor I can gain;
If you will but entertain me,
Perhaps then I might come again.
    O no, John! No, John! No, John! No!

My husband was a Spanish captain,
Went to sea a month ago;
The very last time we kissed and parted,
Bid me always answer no.
    O no, John! No, John! No, John! No!

Madam in your face is beauty,
In your bosom flowers grow;
In your bedroom there is pleasure,
Shall I view it, yes or no?
    O no, John! No, John! No, John! No!

Madam shall I tie your garter,
Tie it a little above your knee;
If my hand should slip a little farther,
Would you think it amiss of me?
    O no, John! No, John! No, John! No!

My love and I went to bed together,
There we lay till cocks did crow;
Unclose your arms my dearest jewel,
Unclose your arms and let me go.
    O no, John! No, John! No, John! No!

31

A May Day Carol

Various May Day carols have been collected in Bedfordshire, Cambridgeshire, Cornwall, and Essex. They all share many of the same elements as the wassail songs, in which a wassail bough, comparable to a May garland, is carried from door to door as a good-luck symbol. This version of the May Day carol is particularly touching; what could be more poetic than the young man, dizzied by the coming of spring, "wandering all this night, and some time of this day," and appearing at the home of the pretty maid early in the morning, bearing a well-budded-out branch of May.

Andante

The moon shines bright, the stars give a light, A lit-tle be-fore 'tis day; Our

Heav-en-ly Fa-ther, He cal-lèd to us, And bid us a-wake and pray. A-

wake, a-wake, oh pret-ty, pret-ty maid, Out of your drow-sy dream; And

32

step in-to your dair-y be-low, And fetch me a bowl of cream.

rit. e dim.

The moon shines bright, the stars give a light,
A little before 'tis day;
Our Heavenly Father, He callèd to us,
And bid us awake and pray.

Awake, awake, oh pretty, pretty maid,
Out of your drowsy dream;
And step into your dairy below,
And fetch me a bowl of cream.

If not a bowl of thy sweet cream,
A cup to bring me cheer;
For the Lord knows when we shall meet
   again,
To go Maying another year.

I have been wandering all this night,
And some time of this day;
And now returning home again,
I've brought you a branch of May.

A branch of May I've brought you here,
And at your door I stand;
'Tis nothing but a sprout, but well budded
   out,
By the work of our Lord's hand.

My song is done and I must be gone,
No longer can I stay;
So it's God bless you all, both great and small,
And send you a joyful May.

The Oak and the Ash

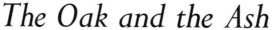

A frequent theme in English folk songs is that of the simple country girl going to the big city and finding it distasteful. There is usually a line to the effect that "the man that I wed must be North Country bred." This tune dates from about 1650; a version of it appeared in the *Fitzwilliam Virginal Book*.

Andante con moto

A North Coun-try maid up to Lon-don had strayed, Al - though with her na-ture it

did not a-gree, Which made her re-pent, and so bit-ter-ly la-ment "Oh I

wish once a - gain for the North Coun - try. Oh the oak and the ash and the

bon-nie i - vy tree, They_ flour - ish at home in my own coun - try!"

A North Country maid up to London had
    strayed,
Although with her nature it did not agree,
Which made her repent, and so bitterly
    lament,
Oh I wish once again for the North Country.

Oh the oak and the ash and the bonnie ivy tree,
They flourish at home in my own country!

O fain would I be in the North Country,
Where the lads and the lasses are making of
    hay;
There should I see what is pleasant to me,
A mischief light on them entic'd me away!
Chorus:

I like not the court, nor the city resort,
Since there is no fancy for such maids as me;
Their pomp and their pride I can never abide,
Because with my humor it does not agree.
Chorus:

How oft have I been in the Westmoreland
    green,
Where the young men and maidens resort for
    to play,
Where we with delight, from morning till
    night,
Could feast it and frolic on each holiday.
Chorus:

The ewes and their lambs, with the kids and
    their dams,
To see in the country how finely they play;
The bells they do ring, and the birds they do
    sing,
And the fields and the gardens are pleasant
    and gay.
Chorus:

At wakes and at fairs, being freed of all cares,
We there with our lovers did use for to dance;
Then hard hap had I, my ill fortune to try,
And so up to London, my steps to advance.
Chorus:

But still I perceive, I a husband might have,
If I to the city my mind could but frame;
But I'll have a lad that is North Country
    bred,
Or else I'll not marry, in the mind that I am.
Chorus:

A maiden I am, and a maid I'll remain,
Until my own country again I do see,
For here in this place I shall ne'er see the face
Of him that's allotted my love for to be.
Chorus:

Then farewell my daddy, and farewell my
    mammy,
Until I do see you, I nothing but mourn;
Rememb'ring my brothers, my sisters, and
    others,
In less than a year I hope to return.
Chorus:

Lavender's Blue

Many a nursery rhyme was far in spirit from the nursery in its earliest version. Here is one, dating from 1672, that has as its prototype a song called "Diddle-diddle, or The Kind Country Lovers." I have eliminated nine verses, not for bowdlerization, but because they incline to dullness.

Allegretto

Lav - en-der's blue dil-ly dil-ly Lav - en-der's green,
When I am king, dil-ly dil-ly You shall be queen.

Some current versions substitute dilly dilly for diddle diddle. Take your choice.

Lavender's blue, diddle diddle,
Lavender's green,
When I am king, diddle diddle,
You shall be queen.

Lavender's green, diddle diddle,
Lavender's blue,
You must love me, diddle diddle,
'Cause I love you.

Down in the vale, diddle diddle,
Where flowers grow,
And the birds sing, diddle diddle,
All in a row.

A brisk young man, diddle diddle,
Met with a maid,
And laid her down, diddle diddle,
Under the shade.

There they did play, diddle diddle,
And kiss and court,
All the fine day, diddle diddle,
Making good sport.

I've heard them say, diddle diddle,
Since I came hither
That you and I, diddle diddle,
Might lie together.

Therefore be kind, diddle diddle,
While here we lie,
And you will love, diddle diddle,
My dog and I.

For you and I, diddle diddle,
Now all are one,
And we will lie, diddle diddle,
No more alone.

Lavender's blue, diddle diddle,
Lavender's green,
Let me be king, diddle diddle,
You be the queen.

Lavender's green, diddle diddle,
Lavender's blue,
You must love me, diddle diddle,
'Cause I love you.

Blow the Wind Southerly

JOHN STOBBS

A traditional Tyneside air from northern England. The words are based on a fragment found in *The Bishoprick Garland.*

Andante

Blow the wind South-er-ly, South-er-ly, South-er-ly, Blow the wind South o'er the

bon-nie blue sea; Blow the wind South-er-ly, South-er-ly, South-er-ly,

Blow bon-nie breeze, my lov-er to me. They told me last night there were

ships in the off-ing, And I hur-ried down to the deep roll-ing sea; But my

eye could not see it wher - ev-er might be it, The bark that is bear-ing my lov-er to me.

poco rit. e dim.

Blow the wind Southerly, Southerly, Southerly,
    Blow the wind South o'er the bonnie blue sea;
Blow the wind Southerly, Southerly, Southerly,
    Blow bonnie breeze, my true lover to me.

They told me last night there were ships in the offing,
    And I hurried down to the deep rolling sea;
But my eye could not see it wherever might be it,
    The bark that is bearing my lover to me.

The Cherry Tree Carol

This is a variation of a well-known ballad collected by James Francis Child (#54). It is believed to be just one episode from a much longer ballad of the Middle Ages which recounted a fanciful story of Christ. No other portions of the ballad have been preserved. Super-religionists have often expressed their annoyance of this portrayal of Saint Joseph as a skeptic. The picture of Joseph as the typical abashed and embarrassed husband is timeless: "And Mary gathered cherries, while Joseph stood around."

Andante con moto

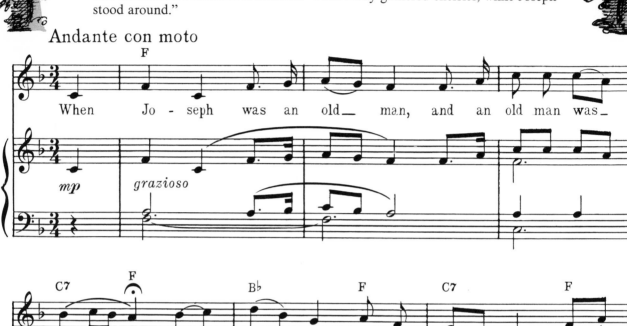

When Jo - seph was an old___ man, and an old man was___

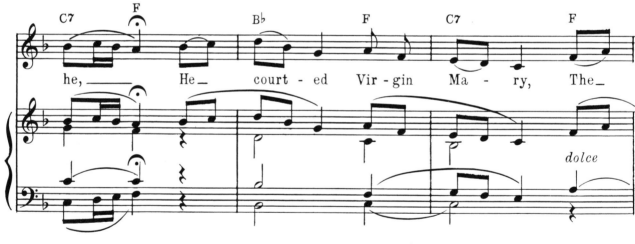

he,___ He___ court - ed Vir - gin Ma - ry, The___

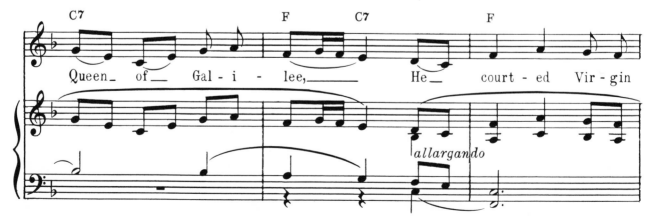

Queen___ of___ Gal - i - lee,___ He___ court - ed Vir - gin

When Joseph was an old man, and an old man was he,
He courted Virgin Mary, the Queen of Galilee,
He courted Virgin Mary, the Queen of Galilee.

Now Joseph and Mary were a-walking one day,
Here is apples and cherries aplenty to behold,
Here is apples and cherries aplenty to behold.

Pick me some cherries, Joseph, pick me some cherries, do,
Pick me some cherries, Joseph, for I am with child,
Pick me some cherries, Joseph, for I am with child.

Then Joseph flew in angry, in angry flew he,
Let the father of your baby gather cherries for you,
Let the father of your baby gather cherries for you.

Then up spoke baby Jesus, all in his mother's womb,
Bow you low down you cherry tree, while Mary gathers some,
Bow you low down you cherry tree, while Mary gathers some.

The cherry tree did bow down so low on the ground,
And Mary gathered cherries, while Joseph stood around,
And Mary gathered cherries, while Joseph stood around.

Then Joseph took Mary all on his left knee,
Pray tell me, pretty baby, when your birthday shall be,
Pray tell me, pretty baby, when your birthday shall be?

On the fifth day of January my birthday shall be,
When the clouds and the elements will tremble with fear,
When the clouds and the elements will tremble with fear.

The Green Bushes

This song features the most easily convinced maiden in all folk-song literature. Her quick change of heart surely indicates some deep dissatisfaction with her "true love." This is an ideal song for Irish tenors, of whatever nationality, and it is sometimes claimed as an Irish song. Two verses from it appeared in John Baldwin Buckstone's play *The Green Bushes,* in 1845, and the full song, when subsequently printed in a broadside, attained great popularity.

Moderato

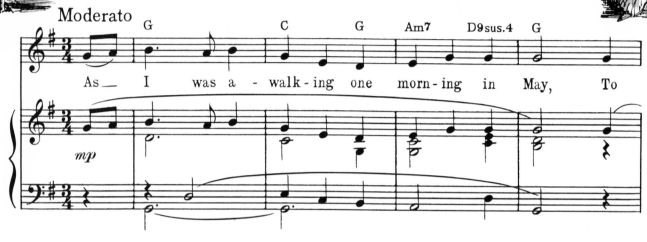

As I was a-walk-ing one morn-ing in May, To

hear the birds whis-tle and see lamb-kins play, I es-

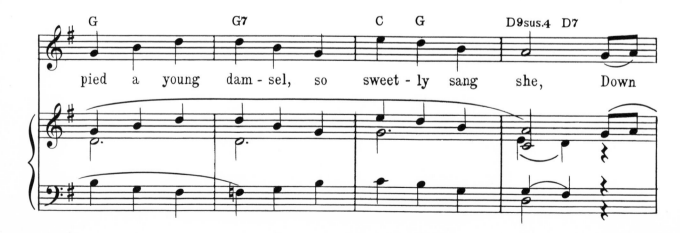

pied a young dam-sel, so sweet-ly sang she, Down

by the green bush - es, where she chanced to meet me.

rit. e dim.

As I was a-walking one morning in May,
    To hear the birds whistle and see lambkins play,
I espied a young damsel, so sweetly sang she,
    Down by the green bushes, where she chanced to meet me.

"Oh, why are you loitering here, pretty maid?"
    "I am waiting for my true love," softly she said.
"Shall I be your true love, and will you agree,
    Down by the green bushes to tarry with me?"

"I will give you fine beavers, and fine silken gowns,
    I will give you smart petticoats, flounced to the ground;
I will give you fine jewels, and live but for thee,
    If you'll leave your own true love and marry with me."

"I want none of your beavers, or fine silken hose,
    For I'm not so poor as to marry for clothes;
But if you be constant and true unto me,
    I'll leave my own true love, and marry with thee.

"Come, let us be going, kind sir, if you please;
    Come, let us be going from under these trees,
For yonder is coming, my true love I see,
    Down by the green bushes, where he thinks to meet me."

And when he came there, and found she was gone,
    He looked very foolish, and cried quite forlorn—
"She's gone with a lover, and forsaken me,
    And left the green bushes, where she vowed to meet me!"

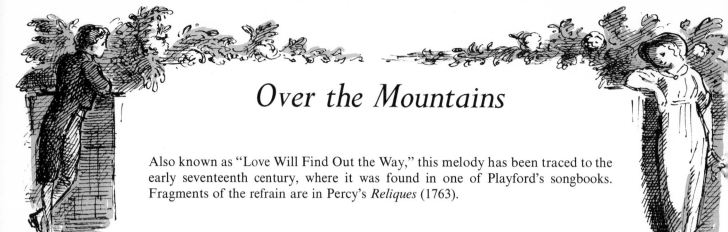

Over the Mountains

Also known as "Love Will Find Out the Way," this melody has been traced to the early seventeenth century, where it was found in one of Playford's songbooks. Fragments of the refrain are in Percy's *Reliques* (1763).

Over the mountains And over the waves,

Under the fountains And under the graves; Under

floods that are deepest, Which Neptune obey, Over

rocks that are_ steep-est, Love will find_ out the way.

Over the mountains
   And over the waves,
Under the fountains
   And under the graves;
Under floods that are deepest,
   Which Neptune obey,
Over rocks that are steepest,
   Love will find out the way.

When there is no place
   For the glow-worm to lie,
When there is no space
   For receipt of a fly;
When the midge dares not venture
   Lest herself fast she lay,
If Love come, he will enter
   And will find out the way.

You may esteem him
   A child for his might;
Or you may deem him
   A coward for his flight;
But if she whom Love doth honor
   Be concealed from the day——
Set a thousand guards upon her,
   Love will find out the way.

Some think to lose him
   By having him confined;
And some do suppose him,
   Poor heart! to be blind;
But if ne'er so close ye wall him,
   Do the best that ye may,
Blind Love, if ye so call him,
   He will find out the way.

You may train the eagle
   To stoop to your fist;
Or you may inveigle
   The Phoenix of the east;
The lioness, you may move her
   To give over her prey;
But you'll ne'er stop a lover——
   He will find out the way.

If the earth it should part him,
   He would gallop it o'er;
If the seas should o'erthwart him,
   He would swim to the shore;
Should his Love become a swallow,
   Through the bright air to stray,
Love will lend wings to follow,
   And will find out the way.

There is no striving
   To cross his intent;
There is no contriving
   His plots to prevent;
But if once the message greet him
   That his True Love doth stay,
If Death should come and meet him,
   Love will find out the way!

Gently, Johnny, My Jingalo

Another song that is found in many variations, some of them tending to be earthy, with lines to the effect that "I put my hand upon her thigh," and so forth. Collected by Cecil Sharp, who wrote that "The words were rather coarse, but I have, I think, managed to re-write the first and third lines of each verse without sacrificing the character of the original song." If one has the time and the inclination, it is surprisingly easy to reconstruct those lines, in endless variety.

Allegretto

I put my hand all in her own, Fair maid is a

lil - y, O! She said: If you love me a - lone

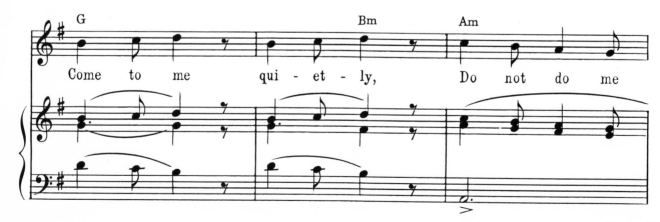

Come to me qui - et - ly, Do not do me

46

in - ju - ry;   Gen - tly, John - ny   my   Jin - ga - lo.

I put my hand all in her own,
  Fair maid is a lilly, O!
She said: If you love me alone
  Come to me quietly,
  Do not do me injury;
  Gently, Johnny, my Jingalo.

I said: You know I love you dear,
  Fair maid is a lilly, O!
She whisper'd softly in my ear:
  Come to me quietly,
  Do not do me injury;
  Gently, Johnny, my Jingalo.

I placed my arm around her waist,
  Fair maid is a lilly, O!
She laugh'd and turn'd away her face:
  Come to me quietly,
  Do not do me injury;
  Gently, Johnny, my Jingalo.

I kiss'd her lips like rubies red,
  Fair maid is a lilly, O!
She blush'd, then tenderly she said:
  Come to me quietly,
  Do not do me injury;
  Gently, Johnny, my Jingalo.

I slipp'd a ring all in her hand,
  Fair maid is a lilly, O!
She said: The Parson's near at hand:
  Come to me quietly,
  Do not do me injury;
  Gently, Johnny, my Jingalo.

I took her to the church next day,
  Fair maid is a lilly, O!
The birds did sing, and she did say:
  Come to me quietly,
  Do not do me injury;
  Gently, Johnny, my Jingalo.

Two Maidens Went Milking One Day

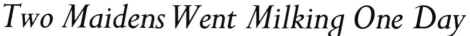

Also known as "Three Maidens Went A-milking," and "The Blackbird in the Bush," this is not the simple country song it might seem at first glance, but an extremely sensual one, rife with sexual symbolism. It dates from the seventeenth century.

Moderato

Two maid - ens went milk - ing one day, _____ Two

maid - ens went milk - ing one day, _____ And the

wind it did blow high, And the wind it did blow low, And it

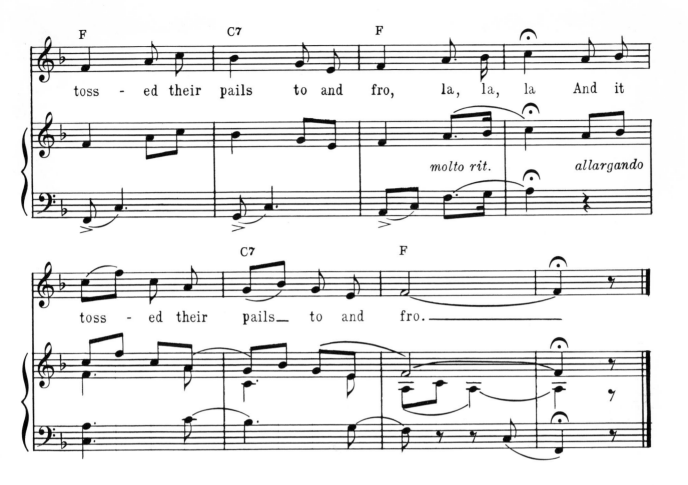

toss - ed their pails to and fro, la, la, la And it

toss - ed their pails__ to and fro. _____

Two maidens went milking one day,
Two maidens went milking one day,
And the wind it did blow high,
And the wind it did blow low,
And it tossèd their pails to and fro, la la la,
And it tossèd their pails to and fro.

They met with a man they did know,
They met with a man they did know,
And they said "Have you the will?"
And they said "Have you the skill,
For to catch us a small bird or two, la la la,
For to catch us a small bird or two?"

"Oh, yes, I got an excellent good skill,
Oh, yes, I got an excellent good skill,
If you will come along with me
Under yonder flowering tree,
I might catch you a small bird or two, la la la,
I might catch you a small bird or two."

So they went and they sat 'neath a tree,
They went and they sat 'neath two,
And the birds flew 'round about,
Pretty birds flew in and out,
And he caught them by one and by two, la
    la la,
And he caught them by one and by two.

Now my boys, let us drink down the sun,
My boys, let us drink down the moon,
Take your lady to the wood
If you really think you should,
You might catch her a small bird or two, la
    la la,
You might catch her a small bird or two.

Cock Robin

There is something troubling about this haunting and poetic children's song; for example, *why* did the sparrow kill poor cock robin? The other animals seem to accept with equanimity the fact that he did so. There are other minor variations of the melody, and other folk rhymes that brush close to it are found far back in antiquity.

Who killed Cock Rob-in? I said the spar-row, With my bow and ar-row, I killed Cock Rob-in. All the birds of the air fell a-sigh-ing and a-sob-bing, When they heard of the death of

poor Cock Rob-in, When they heard of the death of _ poor Cock Rob-in. _

allargando

Who killed Cock Robin?
I, said the sparrow,
With my bow and arrow,
I killed Cock Robin.

*All the birds of the air fell a-sighing and
    a-sobbing,
When they heard of the death of poor Cock
    Robin,
When they heard of the death of poor Cock
    Robin.*

Who saw him die?
I, said the fly,
With my little eye,
I saw him die.
Chorus:

Who'll toll the bell?
I, said the bull,
Because I can pull,
I'll toll the bell.
Chorus:

Who'll dig his grave?
I, said the owl,
With my little trowel,
I'll dig his grave.
Chorus:

Who'll be the parson?
I, said the rook,
With my bell and book,
I'll be the parson.
Chorus:

Who'll be chief mourner?
I, said the dove,
I'll mourn for my love,
I'll be chief mourner.
Chorus:

Died for Love

One of the classic songs of desertion. There are a multitude of variations (A brisk young sailor courted me. . . .) and fragments have broken off and other songs have been formed from them. The Cornish version, "There is a Tavern in the Town," is well known in America.

Pensieroso

A bold young farm - er court - ed me, He gained my heart and my lib - er - ty; He's gained my heart with a free good will, And I must con-fess that I love him still.

poco rit. e dim.

A bold young farmer courted me,
He gained my heart and my liberty;
He's gained my heart with a free good will,
And I must confess that I love him still.

I wish, I wish, but it's all in vain,
I wish I was a maid again,
But a maid again I never shall be,
Since that young farmer lay still with me.

I wish my baby little was born,
And smiling on its father's knee;
And I, poor girl, was dead and gone,
And the green grass growing over me.

There is a house in yonder town,
Where my love goes and sits him down,
And takes some strange girl on his knee,
And he tells her things that he won't tell me.

Go dig my grave long, wide, and deep,
Put a marble stone at my head and feet,
Put over and above a pure white dove,
To let the world know that I died for love.

There is a bird in yonder tree,
Some say he's blind and cannot see,
And I wish it had been the same with me,
When first I met your company.

Buttercup Joe

It would be difficult to find anything more rustic than this Sussex song, although I suspect it has more in it of the music hall than the back pasture. It dates from about the turn of the century.

Now I be a rus-tic sort of chap, My moth-er lives o'er Tha-kem, And my moth-er she's got lots more like I, For her knows how to make 'em

Some they calls I Ba-con Fat, And oth-ers Tur-nip Head__ But I

prove to you I be no mug, Be-cause I'm coun-try bred.—

Chorus

Now I can guide a plow— Milk a cow and I can reap and sow Fresh as the dais-ies in the fields and they calls I But-ter-cup Joe.

Now I be a rustic sort of chap,
 My mother lives o'er Thakem,
And my mother she's got lots more like I,
 For her knows how to make 'em;
Some they calls I Bacon Fat,
 And others Turnip Head,
But I tell to you I be no mug,
 Because I'm country bred.

55

Now I can guide a plow, milk a cow,
    And I can reap and sow;
Fresh as the daisies in the fields,
    And they calls I Buttercup Joe.

Now they gentry folks they laugh to see
    How I eat fat bacon,
They would not touch a bit of it,
    And that's where they're mistaken;
On grogs and wine they do rely
    And take them at their ease;
But give I, a rustic chap,
    A hunk of bread and cheese.
Chorus:

In Summer time, O ain't it prime,
    When we goes out haymaking;
The girls they love to tickle us,
    And freedom it is taken.
Don't they like to rump about,
    Sit on our knees and play,
And don't they like us country chaps
    To roll 'em in the hay.
Chorus:

Have you seen my young woman,
    They calls her our Mary;
She works as busy as a bee
    In farmer Jones' dairy.
And don't she make they dumplings fine,
    By jingo, I mean to try 'em,
And ask her if she won't supply
    A rustic chap like I am.
Chorus:

The Songs of Ireland

Down by the Salley Gardens

WILLIAM BUTLER YEATS

This poem by Yeats was first published in the volume *Crossways* in 1889 and is sometimes printed with the title *An Old Song Resung*. Herbert Hughes, the eminent folk-song scholar, set it to this old air. A salley is a willow tree.

Down_ by the_ sal - ley_ gar - dens my_ love and_ I did meet; She_ passed the_ sal - ley_ gar - dens with_ lit - tle_ snow - white feet. She bid me_ take love

eas - y, as the leaves grow on the tree; But

I, be-ing young and fool - ish, with her did not a-gree.

Down by the salley gardens my love and I did meet;
She passed the salley gardens with little snow-white feet.
She bid me take love easy, as the leaves grow on the tree;
But I, being young and foolish, with her did not agree.

In a field by the river my love and I did stand,
And on my leaning shoulder she laid her snow-white hand.
She bid me take life easy, as the grass grows on the weirs;
But I was young and foolish, and now am full of tears.

Let Erin Remember the Days of Old

THOMAS MOORE

One of the many "unofficial national anthems" of Ireland. Moore set his lyrics to an old tune, "The Red Fox." (Note the close relation it bears to the song "The Little Red Fox" in this collection.) Moore has written how he used to play old airs on the piano for the patriot Robert Emmett, ". . . and I remember his starting up as from a reverie when I finished playing that spirited tune 'The Red Fox,' and exclaiming, 'Oh, that I were at the head of twenty thousand men, marching to that air!'"

Moderato con spirito

Let E-rin re-mem-ber the days of old, Ere her faith-less sons be-tray'd her; When Ma-lach-i wore the— col-lar of gold, Which he won from her proud in-va-der; When her kings with stand-ards of

green un-furl'd, Led the Red-Branch Knights to dan - ger: Ere the

em'-rald gem of the west-ern world Was set in the crown of a stran-ger.

poco rit. e dim.

Let Erin remember the days of old,
   Ere her faithless sons betray'd her;
When Malachi wore the collar of gold,
   Which he won from her proud invader;
When her kings with standards of green unfurl'd
   Led the Red-Branch Knights to danger:
Ere the emerald gem of the western world
   Was set in the crown of a stranger.

On Lough Neagh's bank as the fisherman strays,
   When the clear, cold eve's declining,
He sees the round towers of other days,
   In the wave beneath him shining!
Thus shall memory often, in dreams sublime,
   Catch a glimpse of the days that are over,
Thus, sighing, look through the waves of time
   For the long-faded glories they cover!

Note: Malachi, a King of Ireland in the tenth century, successively defeated in hand-to-hand combat two champions sent against him by the Danes, taking as trophies a sword from one and a collar of gold from the other. *The Red Branch Knights* were a hereditary order of chivalry in Ulster. *Lough (lake) Neagh* is supposed to have originally been a fountain. It overflowed, submerging the entire countryside.

The Cruiskeen Lawn

THE LITTLE FULL JUG

America's "Little Brown Jug" is a distant relation to this song which has been in oral tradition in Scotland and Ireland since the seventeenth century. Robert Burns's "John Anderson, My Jo" has what is practically the same melody. Another version of it appeared in Charles Coffey's *The Beggar's Wedding*, which was Ireland's answer to John Gay's *The Beggar's Opera* and was first performed in 1728.

Con spirito

Let the farm-er praise his grounds, Let the hunts-man praise his hounds, And the shep-herd his sweet-scent-ed lawn; But I, more blest then they, Spend each hap-py night and day With my charm-ing lit-tle cruis-keen lawn, lawn, lawn, Oh, my

Chorus

charm-ing lit-tle cruis-keen lawn. Gra ma chree ma cruis-keen, Slain - te geal ma-vour-neen,

Gra ma chree a cool - in bawn, bawn, bawn, Oh, gra ma chree a cool - in bawn.

poco rit. *a tempo*

Let the farmer praise his grounds,
Let the huntsman praise his hounds,
   And the shepherd his sweet-scented lawn;
But I, more blest than they,
Spend each happy night and day
   With my charming little cruiskeen lawn, lawn,
     lawn,
   Oh, my charming little cruiskeen lawn.

Gra machree ma cruiskeen,
Slainte geal mavourneen,
Gra machree a coolin bawn, bawn, bawn,
Oh, gra machree a coolin bawn.

Note: Phonetically, the chorus is approximately:

Gra-ma-kree ma kroosh-keen
Shlan-ta gal ma-voor-neen
Gra-ma-kree a cool-een bawn, bawn, bawn,
Oh, gra-ma-kree a cool-een bawn.

Translated, it means:

Little jug, my heart's love,
Bright health to my own dove;
Little jug my own heart's love, love, love,
Oh, Little jug my own heart's love!

Immortal and divine,
Great Bacchus, god of wine,
   Create me by adoption thy son;
In hopes that you'll comply
That my glass shall ne'er run dry,
   Nor my smiling little cruiskeen lawn, lawn, lawn,
   My smiling little cruiskeen lawn.
Chorus:

And when grim death appears,
After few but happy years,
   And tells me that my glass it has run;
I'll say, "Begone, ye knave!
For great Bacchus gave me leave,
   To drink another cruiskeen lawn, lawn, lawn,
   To drink another cruiskeen lawn."
Chorus:

Then fill your glasses high,
Let's not part with lips a-dry,
   Though the lark now proclaims it is dawn;
And since we can't remain,
May we shortly meet again,
   To fill another cruiskeen lawn, lawn, lawn,
   To fill another cruiskeen lawn.
Chorus:

63

Shule Aroon

COME, O LOVE   VERSION I

This fine song of lamentation has been traced to the early eighteenth century. The verses refer to a lover's enlistment in the "Wild Geese" of the Irish Brigade (1691–1740), who served with the French, hoping somehow through this eventually to drive the English out of Ireland. The lyrics of the chorus seem to have come from an entirely different kind of song.

Andante con moto

I would I were on yon der hill, 'Tis there I'd sit and cry my fill, And ev-'ry tear would turn a mill, Iss guh day thoo a-voor-neen slawn.

Chorus

Shule, shule, shule a-roon, Shule go suc-cir a-gus shule go kewn, Shule go_ dheen dur-rus og-gus ay-lig_ lume, Iss guh day thoo a-voor-neen_ slawn.

I would I were on yonder hill,
'Tis there I'd sit and cry my fill,
And every tear would turn a mill,
Iss guh day thoo avorneen slawn.

Shule, shule, shule aroon,
Shule go succir agus, shule go kewn,
Shule go dheen durrus oggus aylig lume,
Iss guh day thoo avorneen slawn.

I'll sell my rock, I'll sell my reel,
I'll sell my only spinning-wheel,
To buy for my love a sword of steel,
Iss guh day thoo avorneen slawn.
Chorus:

I'll dye my petticoats, I'll dye them red,
And round the world I'll beg my bread,
Until my parents shall wish me dead,
Iss guh day thoo avorneen slawn.
Chorus:

I wish, I wish, I wish in vain,
I wish I had my heart again,
And vainly think I'd not complain,
Iss guh day thoo avorneen slawn.
Chorus:

But now my love has gone to France,
To try his fortune to advance;
If he e'er come back, 'tis but a chance,
Iss guh day thoo avorneen slawn.
Chorus:

Note: The Gaelic is written phonetically. The Chorus translates:

Come, come, come, O Love,
Quickly come to me, softy move;
Come to the door, and away we'll flee,
And safe for aye may my darling be!

Shule Aroon

COME, O LOVE   VERSION II

This version, as sung by the scholar and folk singer Patrick Galvin, bears a startling resemblance to the last half of the Protestant hymn, "Nearer My God To Thee." It is hard to figure how this came about, since the hymn was hardly ever heard in Catholic Ireland. Whatever the story, it is one of the most hypnotically beautiful songs in the world.

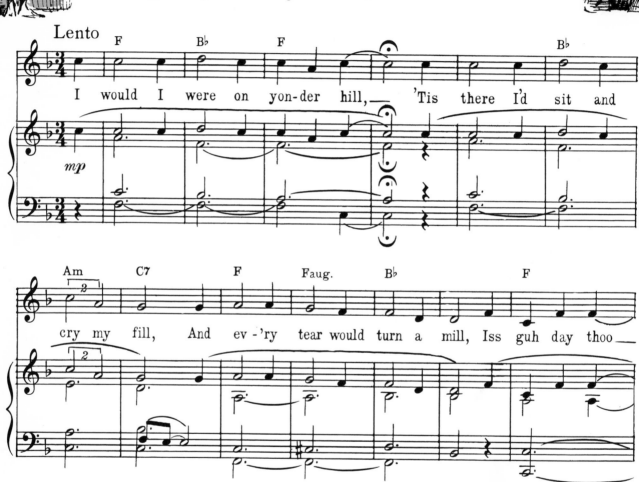

Lento

I would I were on yon-der hill,__ 'Tis there I'd sit and cry my fill, And ev-'ry tear would turn a mill, Iss guh day thoo__ a - voor - neen_ slawn. Shule, shule,_ shule a - roon. Shule go

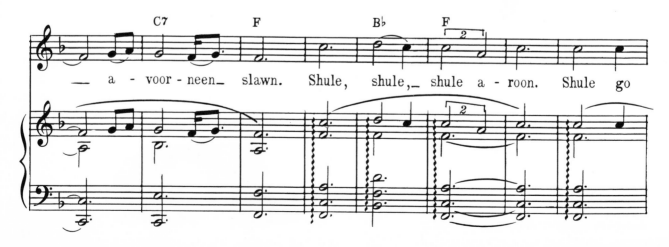

suc - cir a - gus, shule go kewn, Shule go dheen dur - rus og - gus

ay lig lume, Iss guh day thoo a - voor - neen slawn.

I would I were on yonder hill,
'Tis there I'd sit and cry my fill,
And every tear would turn a mill,
Iss guh day thoo avorneen slawn.

Shule, shule, shule aroon,
Shule go succir agus, shule go kewn,
Shule go dheen durrus oggus aylig lume,
Iss guh day thoo avorneen slawn.

I'll sell my rock, I'll sell my reel,
I'll sell my only spinning-wheel,
To buy for my love a sword of steel,
Iss guh day thoo avorneen slawn.
Chorus:

I'll dye my petticoats, I'll dye them red,
And around the world I'll beg my bread,
Until my parents shall wish me dead,
Iss guh day thoo avorneen slawn.
Chorus:

I wish, I wish, I wish in vain,
I wish I had my heart again,
And vainly think I'd not complain,
Iss guh day thoo avorneen slawn.
Chorus:

But now my love has gone to France,
To try his fortune to advance;
If he e'er come back, 'tis but a chance,
Iss guh day thoo avorneen slawn.
Chorus:

Note: The Gaelic is written phonetically. The Chorus translates:

Come, come, come, O Love,
Quickly come to me, softly move;
Come to the door, and away we'll flee,
And safe for aye may my darling be!

67

The Little Red Fox

AN MAIDRÍN RUÁDH

A children's song, from the Gaelic. It is possible that there was allegory intended,
England being the red fox, eating well on Ireland's fat geese.

Allegretto

One— Mon - day— morn - in' I — went— out To
see where my geese did wan - der. The tracks I found up - on— my— ground; The
lit - tle red— fox - 's plun - der. The screech - in' loud did wake me, From

slum - ber I did shake me; And I saw the thief, may he

come — to — grief, For a pau - per — he will make me.

Chorus

Hey, run mod - de - reen a ru ru ru — ru — ru,

In the fog - gy au - tumn weath — er; My geese he's watch - ing

to — sur - prise, With his two — lit - tle ears to - geth - er.

rit.

One Monday mornin' I went out
  To see where my geese did wander.
The tracks I found upon my ground;
  The little red fox's plunder.
The screechin' loud did wake me,
  From slumber I did shake me;
And I saw the thief, may he come to grief,
  For a pauper he will make me.

Hey, run modder-een a ru ru ru ru ru.
In the foggy autumn weather;
My geese he's watching to surprise,
With his two little ears together.

"Good morrow, fox," "Good morrow, Jack."
  "Pray what is that you're eating?"
"'Tis a fine fat goose I stole from you,
  And won't you come and taste him?"
"Oh, no indeed, sir, have no fear,
  I'll haunt the thief and chase him;
I vow and swear you'll dearly pay
  For the fine fat goose you're eating!"
Chorus:

Note: Modder-een a ru (maidrín ruádh), literally translated means "little red dog."

When Pat Came over the Hill

SAMUEL LOVER

Written by the Irish novelist and song writer Samuel Lover, in 1839, this amusing song was widely distributed as a broadside (a cheap one-sheet, reprinting the words of a song) in London, under the title "The Whistling Thief."

And when Pat came ov-er the hill, his col-leen fair to

see, His whis-tle low but shrill the sig-nal was to be;—

— "Oh, Mar-y," the moth-er cried,— "there is some-one whist-ling

When Pat came over the hill, his colleen fair to see,
His whistle low but shrill the signal was to be;
"Oh, Mary," the mother cried, "there is someone whistling sure,"
"Oh, mother, it is the wind you know, that's whistling through the door."

With my fol-diddle-laddle-la,
My fol-diddle-laddle-lee,
With my fol-diddle-laddle-la,
Hey fol-da-lol lol-da-la-lee.

"I've lived a long time, Mary, in this wide world, my dear,
But the door to whistle like that I never yet did hear";
"But, mother, you know the fiddle hangs close beside the chink,
And the wind upon the strings is playing a tune, I think."
Chorus:

"The dog is barking now; the fiddle can't play the tune,"
"But, mother, you know they say dogs bark when they see the moon";
"But how can he see the moon, when he is old and blind,
Blind dogs don't bark at the moon, my dear, nor fiddles don't play with the wind."
Chorus:

"And now I hear the pig, uneasy in his mind,"
"But mother, you know they say that pigs can see the wind";
"That's all very true, my dear, but I think you may remark,
That pigs no more than we can see anything in the dark."
Chorus:

"I'm not such a fool as you think; I know very well 'tis Pat;
Go home you whistlin' thief and do get away out o' that;
And you go into bed, don't play upon me your jeers;
For although I've lost my sight, I haven't lost my ears!"
Chorus:

And you lads when courting going, for your sweethearts' sake,
Take care not to whistle too loud in case the old woman might wake;
From the days when I was young, forget it I never can,
I knew the difference between a fiddle, a dog, and a man.
Chorus:

The Bold Fenian Men

DOWN BY THE GLENSIDE

PEADAR KEARNEY

Brendan Behan, on his record of Irish folk songs, says, "This song was written by a brother of my mother's, and I understand featured in an American film, *West of the Rio Grande.*" It is set to an old air.

Adagio

'Twas down by— the glen-side, I met an old wo-man— A pluck-ing— young net-tles, nor thought I was com-ing;— I list-ened— a-while to the song she was hum-ming,— Glor-y

O, Glor-y O, to the bold Fen - ian men.

'Twas down by the glenside, I met an old woman,
    A'plucking young nettles, nor thought I was coming;
I listened awhile to the song she was humming,
    "Glory O, glory O, to the bold Fenian men!

" 'Tis fifty long years since I saw the moon beaming,
    And strong manly forms, and their eyes with hope gleaming,
I see them again, sure, through all my days dreaming,
    Glory O, glory O, to the bold Fenian men!

"When I was a colleen their marching and drilling,
    Awoke by the glenside sounds awesome and thrilling;
But they loved dear old Ireland, and to die they were willing,
    Glory O, glory O, to the bold Fenian men!

"Some died by the glenside, some died amid strangers,
    And wise men have told us that their cause was a failure;
But they stood by old Ireland, and never feared danger,
    Glory O, glory O, to the bold Fenian men!"

I passed on my way, God be praised that I met her,
    Be life long or short, I shall never forget her;
We may have great men, but we'll never have better,
    Glory O, glory O, to the bold Fenian men!

The Parting Glass

Little is known of the origins of this most beautiful and poignant of all Irish songs. The folk singer Robin Roberts reports that she had heard that a variation of it was the great parting song in Scotland before "Auld Lang Syne" came along.

Andante con moto

O,— all the mon-ey— e'er I had, I— spent it in— good—

com-pa-ny. And— all the harm I've— ev-er done A—

las! it was— to— none but me. And all— I've— done for

want_ of _ wit To mem - 'ry now_ I _ can't re - call So_

fill to me the_ part - ing glass Good_ night and joy_ be_ with you all.

O, all the money e'er I had,
   I spent it in good company.
And all the harm I've ever done
   Alas! it was to none but me.
And all I've done for want of wit
   To mem'ry now I can't recall
So fill to me the parting glass
   Good night and joy be with you all.

O, all the comrades e'er I had,
   They're sorry for my going away,
And all the sweethearts e'er I had,
   They'd wish me one more day to stay,

But since it falls unto my lot,
   I gently rise and softly call,
That I should go and you should not,
   Good night and joy be with you all.

If I had money enough to spend,
   And leisure time to sit awhile,
There is a fair maid in this town,
   That sorely has my heart beguiled.
Her rosy cheeks and ruby lips,
   I own she has my heart in thrall,
Then fill to me the parting glass,
   Good night and joy be with you all.

Bendemeer's Stream

THOMAS MOORE

This is a great favorite on the concert stage, and Percy French's amusing "The Mountains O' Mourne," sung to the same melody, is even more popular with street singers.

Moderato

There's a bow-er of ros-es by Ben-de-meer's stream, And the
time of my child-hood 'twas like a sweet dream, To —

night-in-gale sings 'round it all the day long. In the
sit by the ros-es and hear the bird's song; That —

bow'r and its mu-sic I ne'er can for-get, But oft when a-

lone in the bloom of the year, I think, "Is the night-in-gale sing-ing there yet? Are the ros-es still bright by the calm Ben-de-meer?"

rit. e dim.

There's a bower of roses by Bendemeer's stream,
   And the nightingale sings 'round it all the day long.
In the time of my childhood 'twas like a sweet dream,
   To sit by the roses and hear the bird's song;
That bow'r and its music I ne'er can forget,
   But oft when alone in the bloom of the year,
I think, "Is the nightingale singing there yet?
   Are the roses still bright by the calm Bendemeer?"

The Mountains o' Mourne

PERCY FRENCH

to the tune of "Bendemeer's Stream"

Oh, Mary, this London's a wonderful sight,
    Wid the people here workin' by day and by night.
They don't sow potatoes, nor barley, nor wheat,
    But there's gangs of them diggin' for gold in the street.
At least, when I axed them, that's what I was told,
    So I just took a hand at this diggin' for gold;
But for all that I found there, I might as well be
    Where the Mountains o' Mourne sweep down to the sea.

I believe that, when writin', a wish you expressed,
    As to how the fine ladies in London were dressed;
Well, if you'll believe me, when axed to a ball,
    They don't wear a top to their dresses at all.
Oh, I've seen them myself, and you could not, in thrath,
    Say if they were bound for a ball or a bath;
Don't be startin' them fashions now, Mary Machree,
    Where the Mountains o' Mourne sweep down to the sea.

I seen England's King from the top of a bus—
    I never knew him, though he means to know us;
And though by the Saxon we once were oppressed
    Still I cheered—God forgive me!—I cheered with the rest.
And now that he's visited Erin's green shore,
    We'll be much better friends than we've been heretofore;
When we've got all we want we're as quiet can be,
    Where the Mountains o' Mourne sweep down to the sea.

You remember young Peter O'Loughlin, of course?
    Well, he's over here at the head o' the Force.
I met him today, I was crossin' the Strand
    And he stopped the whole street wid wan wave of his hand;
And there we stood talkin' of days that are gone,
    While the whole population of London looked on;
But for all these great powers, he's wishful, like me,
    To be back where dark Mourne sweeps down to the sea.

There's beautiful girls here—oh, never you mind—
    Wid beautiful shapes nature never designed,
An lovely complexions, all roses and crame,
    But O'Loughlin remarked wid regard to them same:
"Since you're a foine feller, I'll give you a tip;
    Them colors might all come away on your lip."
So I'll wait for the wild rose that's waitin' for me
    Where the Mountains o' Mourne sweep down to the sea.

The Wearing of the Green

"This little song," Frank O'Connor has said, "written in pseudo-Irish dialect, probably by an Ulster Presbyterian and set to what seems to be an adaptation of a Scottish pibroch, is our real national anthem." The anonymous street version of the song, dating from 1798, was slightly altered by the playwright Dion Boucicault some fifty years later, and his version is the one that is generally sung. Napper Tandy was an Irish patriot who was forced to flee the country in 1793.

O Pad-dy dear, and did ye hear the news that's go-in' round? The sham-rock is by law for-bid to grow on I-rish ground! No more Saint Pat-rick's Day we'll keep, his col-or can't be seen, For

there's a cru-el law a-gin' the Wear-in' o' the Green. I

met with Nap-per Tan-dy, and he took me by the hand, And he

said, How's poor ould Ire-land, and how does she stand? She's the

most dis-tress-ful coun-try that ev-er yet was seen, For they're

hang-ing men and wo-men there for the Wear-in' o' the Green.

poco rit. e dim.

"O Paddy dear, and did ye hear the news that's goin' round?
The shamrock is by law forbid to grow on Irish ground!
No more Saint Patrick's Day we'll keep, his color can't be seen,
For there's a cruel law ag'in the Wearin' o' the Green.
I met with Napper Tandy, and he took me by the hand,
And he said, 'How's poor ould Ireland, and how does she stand?'
'She's the most distressful country that ever yet was seen,
For they're hanging men and women there for the Wearin' o' the Green.'

"So if the color we must wear be England's cruel red
Let it remind us of the blood that Irishmen have shed;
And pull the shamrock from your hat, and throw it on the sod,
But never fear, 'twill take root there, though underfoot 'tis trod.
When laws can stop the blades of grass from growin' as they grow,
And when the leaves in summer-time their color dare not show,
Then I will change the color too I wear in my caubeen;
But till that day, please God, I'll stick to the Wearin' o' the Green."

The Rising of the Moon

At the time preceding the rising of 1798, the people hid pikes and guns in their homes and buried them in the bogs. This song, by John Keegan Casey, a Fenian who died in prison at twenty-three, is sung to the tune of "The Wearing of the Green," but faster and louder, with the addition of the following chorus:

> By the rising of the moon,
> By the rising of the moon,
> For the pikes must be together by the rising of the moon.

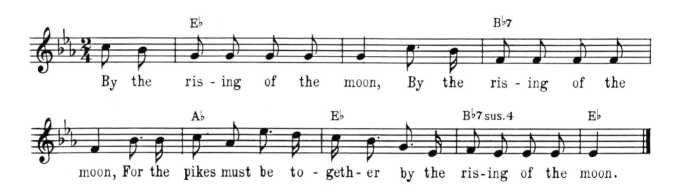

"Oh! then tell me, Sean O'Farrell, tell me why you hurry so?"
"Hush, *ma bouchal,* hush and listen," and his cheeks were all aglow.
"I bear orders from the Captain, get you ready quick and soon,
For the pikes must be together at the rising of the moon."

> *By the rising of the moon,*
> *By the rising of the moon,*
> *For the pikes must be together by the rising of the moon.*

"Oh! then tell me, Sean O'Farrell, where the gathering is to be?"
"In the old spot by the river, right well known to you and me.
One word more—for signal token—whistle up the marching tune,
With your pike upon your shoulder, by the rising of the moon."
Chorus:

Out from many a mud-wall cabin eyes were watching through the night,
Many a manly breast was throbbing for the blessed warning light,
Murmurs passed along the valley like the banshee's lonely croon,
And a thousand blades were flashing at the rising of the moon.
Chorus:

There beside the singing river that dark mass of men was seen,
Far above the shining weapons hung their own immortal green.
"Death to every foe and traitor! Forward! Strike the marching tune,
And, hurrah, my boys, for freedom! 'tis the rising of the moon."
Chorus:

Well they fought for poor old Ireland and full bitter was their fate—
Oh! what glorious pride and sorrow fills the name of Ninety-Eight—
Yet, thank God, while hearts are beating in manhood's burning noon
We will follow in their footsteps at the rising of the moon!
Chorus:

The Lark in the Clear Air

SAMUEL FERGUSON

This tender love song, based on an ancient air, was written by Sir Samuel Ferguson of Belfast some time around 1850. It is extremely popular in Ireland today.

Dear thoughts are_ in my mind, and_ my soul_ soars en-chant-ed As I hear the_ sweet lark sing in_ the clear_ air of the day. For a ten-der, beam-ing_ smile to my hope_ has_ been_ grant-ed, And to-

mor-row she— shall— hear all— my fond— heart would— say.

Dear thoughts are in my mind, and my soul soars enchanted,
As I hear the sweet lark sing in the clear air of the day.
For a tender, beaming smile to my hope has been granted,
And tomorrow she shall hear all my fond heart would say.

I shall tell her all my love, all my soul's adoration,
And I think she will hear me, and will not say me nay.
It is this that gives my soul all its joyous elation,
As I hear the sweet lark sing in the clear air of the day.

I Wish I Had the Shepherd's Lamb

A children's song from, and partly in, the Gaelic.

Allegretto

I wish I had the shep-herd's lamb, the shep-herd's lamb, the shep-herd's lamb, I

wish I had the shep-herd's lamb, and Kat-ey com-ing af — ter

Chorus

Iss O! gur - im, gur - im hoo, Iss grah ma-kree gon kel - lig hoo, Iss

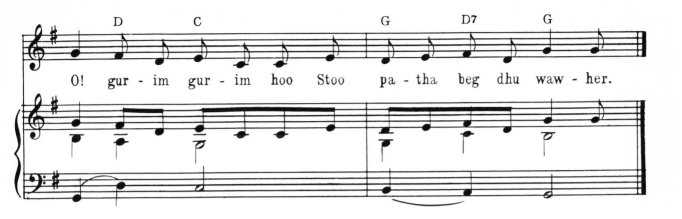

O! gur-im gur-im hoo Stoo pa-tha beg dhu waw-her.

I wish I had the shepherd's lamb, the shepherd's lamb, the shepherd's lamb,
I wish I had the shepherd's lamb, and Katey coming after.

Iss O! gur-im, gur-im hoo,
Iss grah ma-kree gon kellig hoo,
Iss O! gur-im, gur-im hoo.
Stoo pa-tha beg dhu waw-her.

I wish I had the yellow cow, the yellow cow, the yellow cow,
I wish I had the yellow cow, and welcome from my darling.
Chorus:

I wish I had a herd of kine, a herd of kine, a herd of kine,
I wish I had a herd of kine, and Katey from her father.
Chorus:

Note: Chorus, in Gaelic:

Is Ó! goirim, goirim thú,
Is grá mo chroi gan chellig thú,
Is Ó! goirim, goirim thú,
'S tú peata beag do mháthar!
which means, literally, "And O! I call you, I call you, You are my heart's love without deceit . . . and you are mother's little pet!"

O'Donnell Aboo

M. J. McCANN

Another song that is an unofficial national anthem, this rouser, full of references to the locale and leaders of the O'Donnell clan in the sixteenth century, was written in 1843 by a County Mayo college professor. It is sung to a tune composed by an unidentified County Tipperary military-band leader. *Aboo* means "onward" in Gaelic.

Moderato con spirito

Proud-ly the note of the trum-pet is sound-ing,— Loud-ly the war cries a-rise on the gale Fleet-ly the steed by Lough Swil-ly is bound-ing, To join the thick squad-rons in Sai-mears green vale. On ev-'ry moun-tain-eer

90

Strang-ers to flight and fear! Rush to the stand-ards of daunt-less Red Hugh!

Bon-naught and gal-low-glass, Throng from each mountain pass; On for old Er - in, "O'-Don-nell A-boo!"

Proudly the note of the trumpet is sounding,
Loudly the war-cries arise on the gale;
Fleetly the steed by Lough Swilly is bounding,
To join the thick squadrons in Saimear's green vale.
   On, ev'ry mountaineer,
   Strangers to flight and fear!
Rush to the standards of dauntless Red Hugh!
   Bonnaught and gallowglass
   Throng from each mountain pass;
On for old Erin, "O'Donnell Aboo!"

Princely O'Neill to our aid is advancing
With many a chieftain and warrior clan,
A thousand proud steeds in his vanguard are prancing
'Neath the borderers brave from the banks of the Bann;
   Many a heart shall quail
   Under its coat of mail;
Deeply the merciless foeman shall rue,
   When on his ear shall ring,
   Borne on the breezes' wing,
Tir Connell's dread war-cry, "O'Donnell Aboo!"

Wildly o'er Desmond the war-wolf is howling,
Fearless the eagle sweeps over the plain,
The fox in the streets of the city is prowling;
All, all who would scare them are banished or slain.
   Grasp every stalwart hand
   Hackbut and battle brand,
Pay them all back the debt so long due;
   Norris and Clifford well
   Can of Tir Connell tell;
Onward to glory, "O'Donnell Aboo!"

Sacred the cause of Clan Connaill's defending,
The altars we kneel at, the homes of our sires;
Ruthless the ruin the foe is extending,
Midnight is red with the plunderers' fires.
   On with O'Donnell, then,
   Fight the old fight again,
Sons of Tir Connell, all valiant and true.
   Make the false Saxon feel
   Erin's avenging steel!
Strike for your country, "O'Donnell Aboo!"

bonnaught: infantry; *gallowglass:* mercenaries

She Moved through the Fair

PADRAIC COLUM

HERBERT HUGHES

Popular with street singers (and almost everybody else) in Ireland, this song was
written by Padraic Colum and the melody adapted from an old Gaelic air by
Herbert Hughes.

Adagio ad libitum

My young love said to me "My mother won't mind

And my father won't slight you for your lack of kind."

And she stepp'd a-way from me and this she did say, —

"It __ will not be long, love, __ till __ our wed-ding day." __

My young love said to me,
  "My mother won't mind
And my father won't slight you
  for your lack of kind."

And she stepp'd away from me
  and this she did say,
"It will not be long, love,
  till our wedding day."

She stepp'd away from me
  and went thro' the fair,
And fondly I watch'd her
  move here and move there.

And then she went homeward
  with one star awake,
As the swan in the evening
  moves over the lake.

The people were saying
  no two were e'er wed
But one had a sorrow
  that never was said.

And I smiled as she passed
  with her goods and her gear,
And that was the last
  that I saw of my dear.

Last night she came to me,
  she came softly in,
So softly she came
  that her feet made no din.

And she laid her hand on me
  and this she did say,
"It will not be long, love,
  till our wedding day."

Mrs. McGrath

At the time of England's battle against Napoleon, many destitute Irish boys joined the British forces for the sake of food and shelter. This song is a bitter and ruefully witty commentary on that unfortunate situation, much as is the well-known "Johnny, I Hardly Knew Ye." The lady's name is properly pronounced "McGrah."

Allegro

"Oh Mrs.— Mc Grath!" the Ser-geant said, "Would you like to make a sol-dier out of your son, Ted, With a scar-let coat and a big cocked hat, Now Mrs.— McGrath would-n't you like that?"

Chorus

Wid yer too - ri - aa, fol - the - did - dle - aa, Too - ri - oo - ri -

94

oo - ri - aa, Wid yer too - ri - aa, fol - the- did - dle - aa,

Too - ri - oo - ri - oo - ri - aa, Lav beg, the Crack - er, O.

"Oh Mrs. McGrath!" the sergeant said,
"Would you like to make a soldier out of your son,
  Ted,
With a scarlet coat and a big cocked hat,
Now Mrs. McGrath wouldn't you like that?"

Wid yer too-ri-aa, fol-the-diddle-aa,
Too-ri-oo-ri-oo-ri-aa,
Wid yer too-ri-aa, fol-the-diddle-aa,
Too-ri-oo-ri-oo-ri-aa,
Lav beg, the Cracker, O.

So Mrs. McGrath lived on the sea-shore
For the space of seven long years or more
Till she saw a big ship sailing into the bay
"Here's my son Ted, wisha, clear the way."
Chorus:

"Oh, Captain dear, where have ye been
Have ye been sailing on the Mediterreen
Or have ye any tidings of my son Ted
Is the poor boy living or is he dead?"
Chorus:

Then up comes Ted without any legs
And in their place he has two wooden pegs
She kissed him a dozen times or two
Saying, "Holy Moses 'tisn't you."
Chorus:

"Oh then were ye drunk or were ye blind
That ye left yer two fine legs behind
Or was it walking upon the sea
Wore yer two fine legs from the knees away?"
Chorus:

"Oh I wasn't drunk and I wasn't blind
But I left my two fine legs behind
For a cannon ball on the fifth of May
Took my two fine legs from the knees away."
Chorus:

"Oh then Teddy me boy," the widow cried,
"Yer two fine legs were yer mammy's pride
Them stumps of a tree wouldn't do at all
Why didn't ye run from the big cannon ball?
Chorus:

"All foreign wars I do proclaim
Between Don John and the King of Spain
And by herrins I'll make them rue the time
That they swept the legs from a child of mine.
Chorus:

"Oh then, if I had ye back again
I'd never let ye go to fight the King of Spain
For I'd rather my Ted as he used to be
Than the King of France and his whole Navee."
Chorus:

95

Lilli Burlero

This immensely catchy tune first turned up in 1641 in Ulster. In 1688 King James II designated Colonel Richard Talbot, a Catholic, as Earl of Tyrconnel and sent him to Ireland as Lord Lieutenant. This enraged the English and Irish Protestants, who took up this song—"For James is de dog and Tyrconnel's de ass"—as their protest and, as some have it, "shamed James from the throne of England." The melody has been attributed to Henry Purcell, and John Gay used it in *The Beggar's Opera*. It was used as a signature theme by the British Broadcasting Corporation during World War II.

Le -ro le -ro, le -ro le -ro, Lil-li bur-ler -o, bul -len a la.

Ho brother Teague, dost hear de decree?
Lilli burlero, bullen a la;
Dat we shall have a new deputie,
Lilli burlero, bullen a la.

Lero, lero, lilli burlero,
Lilli burlero, bullen a la
Lero lero, lero lero,
Lilli burlero, bullen a la.

Ho, by my Soul, it is a Talbot;
Lilli burlero, bullen a la;
And he will cut all de English throat,
Lilli burlero, bullen a la.
Chorus:

Though, by my soul, de English do prate,
Lilli burlero, bullen a la;
De law's on dere side and de divil knows what,
Lilli burlero, bullen a la.
Chorus:

But if Dispense do come from de Pope,
Lilli burlero, bullen a la;
We'll hang Magna Carta and demselves on a rope,
Lilli burlero, bullen a la.
Chorus:

And de good Talbot is now made a Lord,
Lilli burlero, bullen a la;
And with his brave lads he's coming aboard,
Lilli burlero, bullen a la.
Chorus:

Who all in France have taken a swear,
Lilli burlero, bullen a la;
Dat day will have no Protestant heir,
Lilli burlero, bullen a la.

O but why does he stay behind?
Lilli burlero, bullen a la;
Ho, by my soul, 'tis a Protestant wind,
Lilli burlero, bullen a la.
Chorus:

Now that Tyrconnel is come ashore,
Lilli burlero, bullen a la;
And we shall have Commissions galore,
Lilli burlero, bullen a la.
Chorus:

And he dat will not go to de Mass,
Lilli burlero, bullen a la;
Shall be turned out and look like an ass,
Lilli burlero, bullen a la.
Chorus:

Now, now de hereticks all will go down,
Lilli burlero, bullen a la;
By Christ and St. Patrick's the nation's our own,
Lilli burlero, bullen a la.
Chorus:

Dere was an old prophecy found in a bog,
Lilli burlero, bullen a la;
Dat our land would be ruled by an ass and a dog,
Lilli burlero, bullen a la.
Chorus:

So now dis old prophecy's coming to pass,
Lilli burlero, bullen a la;
For James is de dog and Tyrconnel's de ass,
Lilli burlero, bullen a la.
Chorus:

97

Monday, Tuesday

DIA LUAIN, DIA MAIRT

English lyrics by William Cole

A Gaelic children's song, based on a well-known fairy tale.

Moderato

One— night through the black, Poor Don-all hunch back His cart down the glen-side was bring — ing; When he heard the sweet sound Of the fair-ies all round And this is the song they were sing-ing: Mon-day, Tues-day, Mon-day, Tues-day, Mon-

mp

p meno mosso

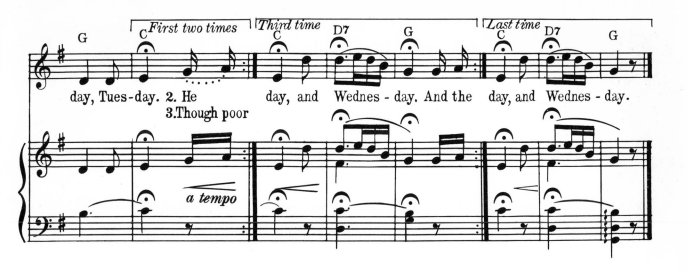

day, Tues-day. 2. He   day, and Wednes - day. And the   day, and Wednes - day.
3.Though poor

One night through the black,
Poor Donall hunch back
His cart down the glenside was bringing;
When he heard the sweet sound
Of the fairies all round
And this is the song they were singing:
Monday, Tuesday;
Monday, Tuesday;
Monday, Tuesday.

He stopped in his track,
Poor Donall hunch back,
At the voices so beautifully blending.
Though the music was sweet
It was quite incomplete,
For they couldn't remember the ending:
Monday, Tuesday;
Monday, Tuesday;
Monday, Tuesday.

Though poor Donall was shy,
He could never stand by
And leave their frustrations unheeded;
So he stifled his fear,
And he sang soft and clear,
Adding the word that they needed:
Monday, Tuesday;
Monday, Tuesday;
Monday, Tuesday, and Wednesday.

And the fairies were glad,
And so grateful he had
Put an end to the song they were voicing,
With their magical knack
Took the hump from his back,
And Donall went homeward rejoicing:
Monday, Tuesday;
Monday, Tuesday;
Monday, Tuesday, and Wednesday.

Note: If you prefer to sing the Gaelic for the refrain, it is phonetically:

Day looin, day mawert,
Day looin, day mawert,
Oggus kaydheen.

mawert is one syllable, almost like *mort*.

Farewell! But Whenever You Welcome the Hour

THOMAS MOORE

The old airs Thomas Moore used were authentic folk music; his lyrics were often, as in this song and "Oft in the Stilly Night," of a more sophisticated nature than would flow out of the folk. This typically poignant lamentation for old friends and times gone by is set to an air that first appeared in Aird's *Selection of Scotch, English, Irish and Foreign Airs,* published in 1788.

Andante

Fare-well! But when-ev-er you_ wel-come the hour, That a - wak-ens the night-song of mirth in your bow'r, Then think of the friend who once wel - com'd it too, And for-got_ his own griefs to be hap - py with you. His griefs may re-turn_ not a

hope may re-main, Of the few that have bright-en'd his path-way of pain— But he

ne'er will for-get the short vis-ion that threw Its en-chant-ment a-round him while ling-'ring with you!

poco rit. e dim.

Farewell! But whenever you welcome the hour,
That awakens the night-song of mirth in your bower,
Then think of the friend who once welcom'd it too,
And forgot his own griefs to be happy with you.
His griefs may return—not a hope may remain
Of the few that have brighten'd his path-way of pain——
But he ne'er will forget the short vision that threw
Its enchantment around him while ling'ring with you!

And still on that evening, when pleasure fills up
To the highest top sparkle each heart and each cup,
Where'er my path lies, be it gloomy or bright,
My soul, happy friends! shall be with you that night;
Shall join in your revels, your sports, and your wiles,
And return to me, beaming all o'er with your smiles!——
Too blest, if it tells me that, 'mid the gay cheer,
Some kind voice has murmur'd "I wish he were here!"

Let Fate do her worst, there are relics of joy,
Bright dreams of the past, which she cannot destroy;
And which come in the night-time of sorrow and care,
To bring back the features that joy us'd to wear.
Long, long be my heart with such memories fill'd!
Like the vase, in which roses have once been distill'd——
You may break, you may ruin the vase, if you will,
But the scent of the roses will hang round it still.

Kevin Barry

This today is the most popular Irish rebel song, especially in America. Kevin Barry, an eighteen-year-old Trinity College student, was captured on the streets of Dublin during an attack on British troops and was hanged on November 1, 1920. Ironically, the tune is an English one: "Rolling Home to Merry England."

In Mount-joy jail one Mon-day morn-ing, High up - on the gal-lows tree Kev-in Bar - ry gave his young life, For the cause of lib-er - ty, But a lad of eight-een sum-mers, Yet no one can de-

ny As he walked to death that morn-ing, He proud-ly held his head on high.

In Mountjoy jail one Monday morning,
　High upon the gallows tree
Kevin Barry gave his young life,
　For the cause of liberty,
But a lad of eighteen summers,
　Yet no one can deny
As he walked to death that morning,
　He proudly held his head on high.

Just before he faced the hangman,
　In his dreary prison cell,
British soldiers tortured Barry,
　Just because he would not tell
The names of his brave companions,
　And other things they wished to know,
"Turn informer or we'll kill you,"
　Kevin Barry answered "No."

Calmly standing to attention,
　While he bade his last farewell
To his broken-hearted mother,
　Whose grief no one can tell.
For the cause he proudly cherished,
　This sad parting had to be;
Then to death walked softly smiling,
　That old Ireland might be free.

Another martyr for old Ireland,
　Another murder for the crown,
Whose brutal laws may kill the Irish,
　But can't keep their spirit down.
Lads like Barry are no cowards,
　From the foe they will not fly,
Lads like Barry will free Ireland,
　For her sake they'll live and die.

Kilgary Mountain

THERE'S WHISKEY IN THE JAR

This is the "Americanized" version of the Irish street ballad "There's Whiskey in the Jar." No Kilgary Mountain exists in Ireland.

Moderato

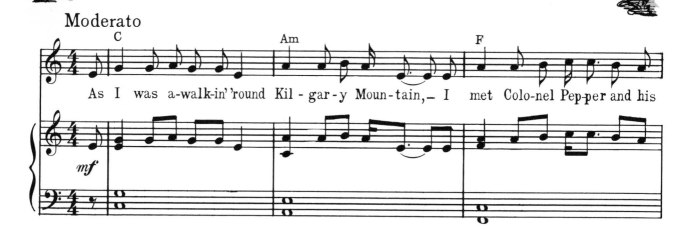

As I was a-walkin' 'round Kil - gar-y Moun-tain,— I met Colo-nel Pep-per and his

mon-ey he was count-in',— I rat-tled— me pis-tols and I drew forth me sa-ber, Say-in',

Meno mosso

"Stand and de-liv-er, for I am the bold de-ceiv-er!" Mush-a rig um du rum da,

Whack fol — the dad-dy O, Whack fol — the dad-dy O, There's whis-key in the jar.

As I was a-walkin' 'round Kilgary Mountain,
I met Colonel Pepper and his money he was
  countin',
I rattled me pistols and I drew forth me saber,
Sayin', "Stand and deliver, for I am the bold
  deceiver!"

Musha rig um du rum da,
Whack fol the daddy O,
Whack fol the daddy O,
There's whiskey in the jar!

The shinin' golden coins did look so bright and
  jolly,
I took 'em with me home and I gave 'em to my
  Molly;
She promised and she vowed that she never would
  deceive me,
But the divil's in the women and they never can
  be easy.
Chorus:

When I was awakened between six and seven,
The guards were all around me in numbers odd
  and even;
I flew to my pistols, but alas! I was mistaken,
For Molly's drawn my pistols and a prisoner I was
  taken.
Chorus:

They put me in jail without judge or writin'
For robbing Colonel Pepper on Kilgary Mountain,
But they didn't taken my fists so I knocked the
  sentry down,
And bid a fond farewell to the jail in Slaigo town.
Chorus:

Now some take delight in fishin' and bowlin',
And others take delight in their carriages a-rollin',
But I take delight in the juice of the barley
And courtin' pretty girls in the mornin' so early.
Chorus:

105

Oft in the Stilly Night

THOMAS MOORE

The most beautiful and poignant of Thomas Moore's songs, it's a matter of controversy how much of a "folk" song this is. There are those who maintain it is a "drawing room" or "platform" song. But folks sing it. It was a great favorite in those good old days when families would sing around the piano together of an evening.

Oft in the still-y night, Ere slum-ber's chain has bound me,

Fond mem-'ry brings the light Of oth-er days a - round me, The smiles, the tears, of

boy-hood's years, The words of love then spo - ken, The eyes that shone, now dimm'd and gone, The

cheer-ful hearts now bro-ken! Thus, in the still-y night, Ere slum-ber's chain has

bound me, Sad mem-'ry brings the light Of oth-er days a-round me.

Oft in the stilly night,
　Ere slumber's chain has bound me,
Fond mem'ry brings the light
　Of other days around me,
The smiles, the tears, of boyhood's years,
　The words of love then spoken,
The eyes that shone, now dimm'd and gone,
　The cheerful hearts now broken!
Thus, in the stilly night,
　Ere slumber's chain has bound me,
Sad mem'ry brings the light
　Of other days around me.

When I remember all
　The friends, so link'd together,
I've seen around me fall,
　Like winds in wintry weather,
I feel like one who treads alone
　Some banquet hall deserted,
Whose lights are fled, whose garlands dead,
　And all but he departed!
Thus, in the stilly night,
　Ere slumber's chain has bound me,
Sad mem'ry brings the light
　Of other days around me.

Molly Brannigan

As sometimes happens with parodies, this music-hall satire on sentimental Irish songs has had more staying power (and has more genuine pathos) than the songs it is mimicking.

Recitativo

Gm · Dm · A7 · Dm

Ma'am dear, did ye nev-er hear of pret-ty Mol-ly Bran-ni-gan_ In

F · Gm · A7 · Dm

throth, then, she's left me and I'll nev-er be a man a-gain_

Gm · Dm · A7 · Dm

Not a spot on my hide will a sum-mer's sun e'er tan a-gain,_ Since

Mol - ly's gone and left me here a - lone for to die. The place where my heart was you'd ais - y rowl a tur - nip in, 'Tis as large as all Dub - lin, and from Dub - lin to the Div - il's Glen,_ If she wish'd to take an - oth - er, sure she might have left mine back a - gain,_ And

not have gone and left me here a - lone for to die.

Ma'am dear, did ye never hear of pretty Molly Brannigan?
In troth, then, she's left me and I'll never be a man again.
Not a spot on my hide will a summer's sun e'er tan again,
Since Molly's gone and left me here alone for to die.

The place where my heart was you'd aisy rowl a turnip in,
'Tis as large as all Dublin, and from Dublin to the Divil's glen;
If she wish'd to take another, sure she might have left mine back again,
And not have gone and left me here alone for to die.

Ma'am dear, I remember when the milking time was past and gone,
We strolled thro' the meadow, and she swore I was the only one
That ever she could love, but oh! the base and cruel one,
For all that she's left me here alone for to die.

Ma'am dear, I remember when coming home the rain began,
I wrapt my frieze-coat round her and ne'er a waistcoat had I on;
And my shirt was rather fine-drawn, but oh! the false and cruel one,
For all that she's left me here alone for to die.

The left side of my carcase is as weak as water gruel, ma'am,
There's not a pick upon my bones, since Molly's proved so cruel, ma'am;
Oh! if I had a blunder gun, I'd go and fight a duel, ma'am,
For sure I'd better shoot myself than live here to die.

I'm cool an' determined as any salamander, ma'am,
Won't you come to my wake when I go the long meander, ma'am?
I'll think myself as valiant as the famous Alexander, ma'am,
When I hear ye cryin' o'er me, "Arrah! why did ye die?"

110

John O'Dwyer of the Glen

Translated from the Gaelic by Frank O'Connor

This magnificant and difficult song comes from the mid-seventeenth century. The O'Dwyers were one of the great County Tipperary landowning families whose woodlands were cut down by Cromwell's occupying forces. This deliberate despoliation of the land was in part a measure to prevent guerrilla warfare.

Andante con moto

When once I rose at morn-ing The sum-mer sun was shin-ing,— I heard the horn a-wind-ing And the birds' mer-ry songs; There were badg-er and wea-sel,— Wood-cock and plov-er,— And

ech - o re - peat - ing The mu - sic of the guns The

hunt - ed fox was flag - ging___ The horse-men fol - lowed shout - ing,___

Count-ing her geese___ on the high-way Some wom-an's heart was sore; But

now the woods are fall - ing,___ We must go ov - er the wa - ter

112

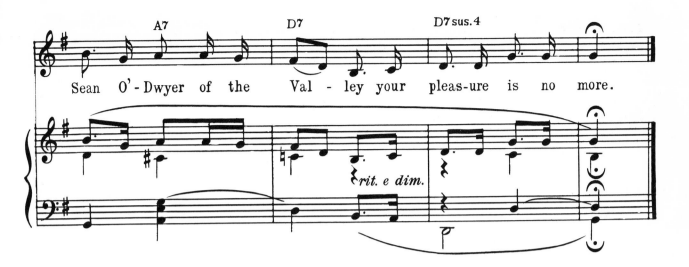

Sean O'-Dwyer of the Val - ley your pleas-ure is no more.

rit. e dim.

When once I rose at morning
The summer sun was shining,
I heard the horn awinding
   And the birds' merry songs;
There were badger and weasel,
Woodcock and plover,
And echo repeating
   The music of the guns.
The hunted fox was flagging,
The horsemen followed shouting;
Counting her geese on the highway
   Some woman's heart was sore;
But now the woods are falling
We must go over the water—
Sean O'Dwyer of the Valley
   Your pleasure is no more.

There's cause enough for grieving,
All the woodlands falling,
The north wind comes freezing
   With death in the sky;
My merry hound's tied tightly
From sporting and chasing
That would lift a young lad's sorrows
   In noondays gone by.
The stag is up in Carrick,
His antlers high as ever;
He can enjoy the heather,
   But our day is o'er;
Let the townsmen cease their prying,
And I'll take ship from Galway—
Sean O'Dwyer of the Valley,
   Your pleasure is no more.

The homes of Coomasrohy
Have neither roof nor gable,
In Strade where birds are silent
   No man recites its praise;
From Clonmel along the river
There is no shade nor shelter,
And hares amid the clearings
   Run safe all their days.
What is this thud of axes,
Trees creaking and falling,
The sweet thrush and the blackbird
   In silence everywhere?
And—certain sign of trouble—
Priests and their people
Flying to mountain valleys
   To raise the word of prayer?

My only wish on waking
Is that I had ceased from caring
Before my own demesne lands
   Were cause for my grief;
For through long days of summer
I rambled through their orchards
And oakwoods all green
   With the dew on the leaf;
And now that I have lost them
And lonesome among strangers
I sleep among the bushes
   Or mountain caves alone,
Either I'll find some quiet
To live as best contents me
Or leave them all behind me
   For other men to own.

The Time I've Lost in Wooing

THOMAS MOORE

This jaunty song of a man's rueful resignation to the powers of love is based on an air called "Pease Upon a Trencher." The "sprite" in the second verse is a leprechaun who, as long as you fix your gaze on him, will stay put, but who is also extremely ingenious in getting you to look away—and he's off.

Allegretto

The time I've lost in woo - ing, In watch-ing and pur - su - ing The light that lies In wo-man's eyes, Has been my heart's un - do - ing. Though wis - dom oft has sought me, I scorn'd the lore she brought me, My

on - ly books Were wo-man's looks, And fol - ly's all they've taught me.

The time I've lost in wooing,
In watching and pursuing
   The light that lies
   In woman's eyes,
Has been my heart's undoing.
Though wisdom oft has sought me,
I scorn'd the lore she brought me,
   My only books
   Were woman's looks,
And folly's all they've taught me.

Her smile when beauty granted,
I hung with gaze enchanted,
   Like him, the sprite,
   Whom maids by night
Oft meet in glen that's haunted.

Like him, too, beauty won me,
But while her eyes were on me,
   If once their ray
   Was turned away,
Oh! winds could not outrun me.

And are these follies going?
And is my proud heart growing
   Too cold or wise
   For brilliant eyes
Again to set it glowing?
No—vain, alas! th' endeavor
From bonds so sweet to sever;
   Poor wisdom's chance
   Against a glance
Is now as weak as ever!

The Croppy Boy

One of the best-known songs of the rising of 1798. One explanation for "croppy" is that it was the name given to the peasant rebels in Wexford, who wore their hair closely cropped. "Lord Cornwall" was Lord Cornwallis, Lord Lieutenant of Ireland, and Dungannon was a government prison.

Recitativo

'Twas ear - ly, ear - ly in the Spring, The birds did whis - tle and sweet - ly sing, Chang - ing their notes from tree to tree, ___ And the

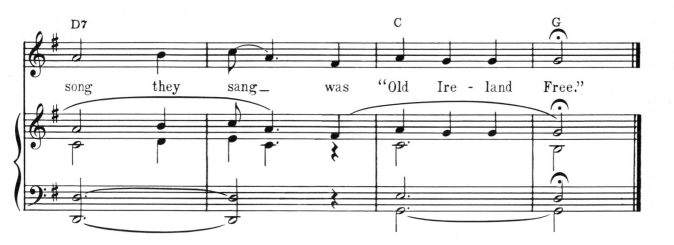

song   they   sang   was "Old   Ire - land   Free."

'Twas early, early in the Spring,
The birds did whistle and sweetly sing,
Changing their note from tree to tree,
And the song they sang was old Ireland free.

'Twas early, early in the night,
The yeoman cavalry gave me a fright;
The yeoman cavalry was my downfall,
And taken was I by the Lord Cornwall.

'Twas in the guard-house where I was laid,
And in the parlor where I was tried;
My sentence passed and my courage low,
When to Dungannon I was forced to go.

As I was passing my father's door,
My brother William stood at the door;
My agèd father stood there also,
My tender mother her hair she tore.

As I was going up Wexford Street,
My own first cousin I chanced to meet;
My own first cousin did me betray,
And for one bare guinea swore my life away.

As I was going up Wexford Hill
Who could blame me to cry my fill?
I looked behind and I looked before,
My agèd mother I shall see no more.

As I was mounted on the scaffold high,
My agèd father was standing by;
My agèd father did me deny,
And the name he gave me was the Croppy Boy.

It was in Dungannon this young man died,
And in Dungannon his body lies;
And you good people that do pass by,
Oh shed a tear for the Croppy Boy.

The Banks of the Roses

This song, from Limerick at the end of the eighteenth century, contains a sentiment found in the folk songs of all countries—to the effect that "them as don't like me can leave me alone." There are those who maintain that the first verse contains sexual symbolism.

Moderato

On the Banks of the Ros - es,— my love and I sat down, And I took out my vi - o - lin to play my love a tune, In the mid - dle of the tune,— Oh, she sighed— and she

said O - ro, John - ny, love - ly John - ny, would you leave me.

rit. e dim.

On the Banks of the Roses, my love and I sat down,
And I took out my violin to play my love a tune,
In the middle of the tune, Oh, she sighed and she said,
 O-ro, Johnny, lovely Johnny, would you leave me?

Oh, when I was a young man I heard my father say,
That he'd rather see me dead and buried in the clay,
Sooner than be married to any runaway,
 By the lovely sweet Banks of the Roses.

Oh, then I am no runaway and soon I'll let them know,
I can take a good glass or can leave it alone;
And the man that doesn't like me he can keep his daughter at home
 And young Johnny will go roving with another.

And if ever I get married 'twill be in the month of May,
When the leaves they are green and the meadows they are gay;
And I and my true love can sit and sport and play
 On the lovely sweet Banks of the Roses.

The Bard of Armagh

The words set to this old melody are sometimes ascribed to Thomas Campbell, who is said to have written it in 1801. Padraic Colum writes of it: ". . . the picture it calls up is altogether wrong. A harper would know that he was the custodian of an aristocratic art and would never remind an audience that he was once a boy of the countryside." Nevertheless, it is a touching song of remembered youth.

Oh! List to the tale of a poor I-rish harp-er, And scorn not the strings in his old with-ered hand; But re-

mem - ber those fing-ers could once move more sharp-er, To

wa - ken the ech - oes of his dear na - tive land.

rit. e dim.

Oh! List to the tale of a poor Irish harper,
And scorn not the strings in his old withered hand;
But remember those fingers could once move more sharper,
To waken the echoes of his dear native land.

How I long for to muse on the days of my boyhood,
Though four score and three years have fled by since then;
Still it gives sweet reflections, as every young joy should,
That merry-hearted boys make the best of old men.

At wake or at fair I would twirl my shillelah,
And trip through the jig in my brogues bound with straw;
And all the pretty maidens from the village and the valley,
Loved the bold Phelim Brady, the Bard of Armagh.

And when Sergeant Death in his cold arms shall embrace me,
O lull me to sleep with sweet Erin go bragh;
By the side of my Kathleen, my own love, then place me,
And forget Phelim Brady, the Bard of Armagh.

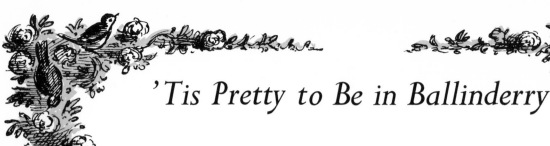

'Tis Pretty to Be in Ballinderry

This first appeared, as "Ballinderry and Chorus," in Edward Bunting's collection of old Irish airs in 1840. *Och hone* is a sound of melancholy reminiscence. "Phelimy Diamond" is sometimes printed as "Phely, my diamond."

Moderato

'Tis pret-ty to be in Bal - lin-der - ry, 'Tis pret-ty to be in Ag - ha -lee, 'Tis pret-tier to be in bon - ny Rams Is - land Sit - ting un-der an i - vy tree.

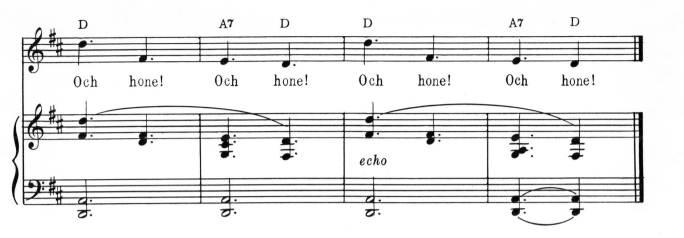

Och hone! Och hone! Och hone! Och hone!

echo

'Tis pretty to be in Ballinderry,
'Tis pretty to be in Aghalee
'Tis prettier to be in bonny Rams Island
Sitting under an ivy tree.
    Och hone! Och hone! Och hone! Och hone!

Oh, that I was in little Rams Island
Oh, that I was with Phelimy Diamond!
He would whistle, and I would sing,
Till we would make the whole island ring.
    Och hone! Och hone! Och hone! Och hone!

123

Whack Fol the Diddle

PEADAR KEARNEY

It is easy to see why the English considered this song (and others by Peadar Kearney) as "seditious" during the time of "the Troubles" in 1916 and after. It is a fine example of ridicule used as a weapon.

Allegretto

I'll sing you a song of Peace and Love, Whack fol the did-dle lol the di-do day. To the land that reigns all lands a-bove Whack fol the did-dle lol the di-do day. May peace and plen-ty be her share, Who kept our home from want and care, Oh,

I'll sing you a song of Peace and Love,
Whack fol the diddle lol the dido day.
To the land that reigns all lands above,
Whack fol the diddle lol the dido day.
May peace and plenty be her share,
Who kept our homes from want and care,
Oh, "God bless England" is our prayer,
Whack fol the diddle lol the dido day.

Whack fol the diddle lol the dido day,
So we say, Hip Hurray!
Come and listen while we pray
Whack fol the diddle lol the dido day.

When we were savage, fierce and wild,
Whack fol the diddle lol the dido day,
She came as a mother to her child,
Whack fol the diddle lol the dido day.
She gently raised us from the slime,
Kept our hands from hellish crime,
And sent us to Heaven in her own good time,
Whack fol the diddle lol the dido day.
Chorus:

Our fathers oft were naughty boys,
Whack fol the diddle lol the dido day.
Pikes and guns are dangerous toys,
Whack fol the diddle lol the dido day.
From Beal-'n-ath Buidhe to Peter's Hill
They made poor England weep her fill,
But old Brittania loves us still,
Whack fol the diddle lol the dido day.
Chorus:

Oh, Irishmen, forget the past,
Whack fol the diddle lol the dido day,
And think of the day that is coming fast,
Whack fol the diddle lol the dido day.
When we shall all be civilized,
Neat and clean and well advised,
Oh, won't Mother England be surprised,
Whack fol the diddle lol the dido day.
Chorus:

The Songs of Scotland

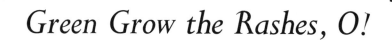

Green Grow the Rashes, O!

ROBERT BURNS

This heartfelt tribute to womanhood is set to a tune Burns found in *Walsh's Country Dances,* published in 1740. Another version of the lyrics is in *The Merry Muses of Caledonia,* a group of folk poems which Burns collected, edited, and often rewrote.

Moderato

There's naught but care on ev-'ry han', In ev-'ry hour that pass-es, O! What

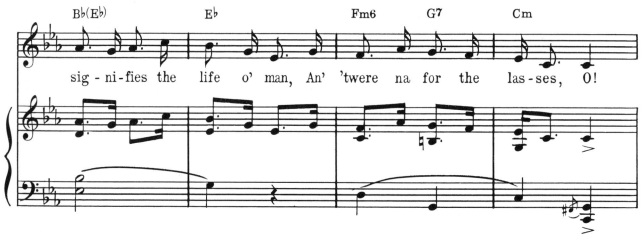

sig - ni-fies the life o' man, An' 'twere na for the las-ses, O!

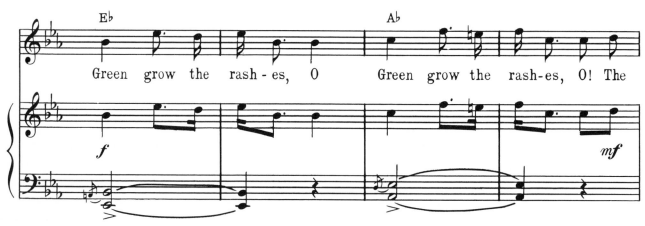

Green grow the rash - es, O Green grow the rash - es, O! The

128

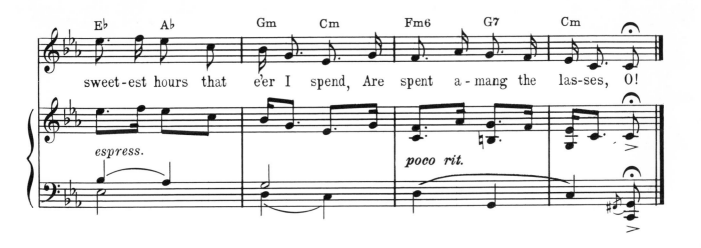

sweet-est hours that e'er I spend, Are spent a-mang the las-ses, O!

espress.

poco rit.

There's naught but care on ev'ry han',
 In ev'ry hour that passes, O!
What signifies the life o' man,
 An' 'twere na for the lasses, O!

Green grow the rashes, O!
 Green grow the rashes, O!
The sweetest hours that e'er I spend,
 Are spent among the lasses, O!

The wardly race may riches chase,
 An' riches still may fly them, O;
An' though at last they catch them fast,
 Their hearts can ne'er enjoy them, O.
Chorus:

Gie me a cannie hour at e'en,
 My arms about my dearie, O,
An' warldly cares, an warldly men
 May a' gae tapsalteerie, O!
Chorus:

An' you sae douce, wha sneer at this,
 Ye're naught but senseless asses, O!
The wisest man the warld e'er saw,
 He dearly lo'ed the lasses, O!
Chorus:

Auld nature swears the lovely dears
 Her noblest work she classes, O,
Her 'prentice han' she tried on man,
 An' then she made the lasses, O.
Chorus:

cannie: quiet. *tapsalteerie:* topsy-turvy. *douce:* sober.

Wae's Me for Prince Charlie

WILLIAM GLEN

No man in history has had as many songs written about him as Bonnie Prince Charlie. Known as "the Young Pretender," and "the Chevalier," Charles Edward Stuart (1720–88), young, dashing, and courageous, led the Second Jacobite Rebellion in 1745. His intent was to restore the Stuarts to the throne of England and Scotland. After many heartening victories, he was finally routed at the Battle of Culloden, sent into hiding, and eventually escaped to France. The lyrics to this beautiful old melody were written by William Glen (1789–1826), a Glasgow man who has apparently written nothing else.

A wee bird cam' to our ha' door, He warbled sweet and clearly, An' aye the o'er-come o' his sang Was "Wae's me for Prince Charlie!" Oh! when I heard the

bon-nie, bon-nie bird, The tears cam' drap-pin rare-ly, I took my bon-net aff my head, For weel I lo'ed Prince Char-lie!

poco rit. e dim.

A wee bird cam' to our ha' door,
   He warbled sweet and clearly,
An' aye the o'er-come o' his sang
   Was "Wae's me for Prince Charlie!"
Oh! when I heard the bonnie, bonnie bird,
   The tears cam' drappin rarely,
I took my bonnet aff my head,
   For weel I lo'ed Prince Charlie!

Quoth I, "My bird, my bonnie, bonnie bird,
   Is that a sang ye borrow;
Are those some words ye've learnt by heart,
   Or a lilt o' dool an' sorrow?"
"Oh! no, no, no," the wee bird sang,
   "I've flown sin' mornin' early;
But sic a day o' wind an' rain——
   Oh! wae's me for Prince Charlie!

"On hills that are by right his ain,
   He roves a lanely stranger,
On every side he's press'd by want,
   On every side is danger.

Yestreen I met him in a glen,
   My heart maist burstit fairly,
For sadly changed indeed was he——
   Oh! wae's me for Prince Charlie!

"Dark night cam' on, the tempest roar'd,
   Loud o'er hills an' valleys,
An' where was't that your Prince lay down,
   Wha's hame should been a palace?
He row'd him in a Highland plaid,
   Which cover'd him but sparely,
An' slept beneath a bush o' broom——
   Oh! wae's me for Prince Charlie!"

But now the bird saw some red coats,
   An' he shook his wings wi' anger,
"Oh! this is no a land for me;
   I'll tarry here nae langer!"
He hover'd on the wing a while
   Ere he departed fairly,
But weel I mind the farewell strain
   Was "Wae's me for Prince Charlie!"

ha' door: hall door. *o'er-come:* refrain. *wae's me:* woe is me. *dool:* tragedy. *row'd:* rolled, wrapped. 131

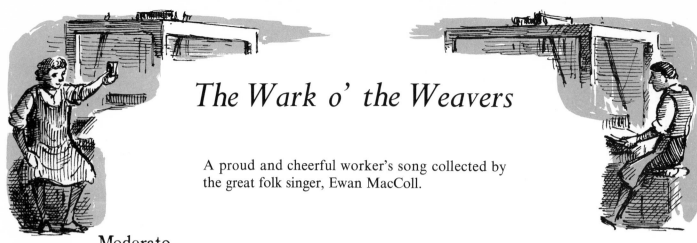

The Wark o' the Weavers

A proud and cheerful worker's song collected by
the great folk singer, Ewan MacColl.

Moderato

We're a' met the-gith-er here to sit and to crack, Wi' oor glass-es in oor hands and oor

wark up-on oor back; And there's no trade a-mang them a' can eith-er mend or mak' If it

was-na for the wark o' the weav - ers. If it was-na for the weav-ers,

what would they do? We would-na ha'e claith made o' oor woo', We would-na ha'e a coat, neith-er black nor blue, Gin it was-na for the wark o' the weav-ers.

We're a' met thegither here to sit and to crack,
Wi' oor glasses in oor hands and oor wark upon
   oor back;
And there's no trade amang them a' can either
   mend or mak'
If it wasna for the wark o' the weavers.

If it wasna for the weavers, what would they do?
We wouldna ha'e claith made o' oor woo',
We wouldna ha'e a coat, neither black nor blue,
Gin it wasna for the wark o' the weavers.

The hireman chiels they mock us and crack aye aboot's,
They say we are thin-faced, bleached-like cloots;
But yet for a' their mockery they canna dae wi'oot's,
Na! They canna want the wark o' the weavers.
Chorus:

There's oor wrichts and oor slaters and glaziers and a',
Oor doctors and oor ministers and them that live by law,
And oor friends in Sooth Ameriky, though them we never saw,
But we ken they wear the wark o' the weavers.
Chorus:

There's oor sailors and oor sodgers, we ken they're a' bauld,
But if they hadna claes, faith, they couldna fecht for cauld;
The high and low, the rich and puir, a'body young and auld—
They winna want the wark o' the weavers.
Chorus:

There's folk that's independent o' ither tradesmen's wark,
The women need nae barber and dykers need nae clerk;
But none o' them can dae wi'oot a coat or a sark,
Na! They canna want the wark o' the weavers.
Chorus:

The weaving is a trade that never can fail,
As lang's we need ae cloot to keep anither hale;
So let us aye be merry ower a bicker o' guid ale,
And drink tae the health o' the weavers.
Chorus:

crack: converse. *chiels:* fellows. *aye aboot's:* talk about us. *wrichts:* wrights, carpenters. *bauld:* bold. *dykers:* wall builders.
sark: shirt. *bicker:* small wooden bowl, cup.

Flow Gently, Sweet Afton

ROBERT BURNS

ALEXANDER HUME

Also known as "Afton Water," there are at least three well-known melodies to this.
It is a matter of taste whether this one is more beautiful than that of the Christmas
carol, "Away in a Manger," which is frequently sung to these lyrics.

Flow gen - tly, sweet Af - ton, a - mang thy green braes, Flow
gen - tly, I'll sing thee a song in thy praise; My
Ma - ry's a - sleep by thy mur - mur - ing stream, Flow

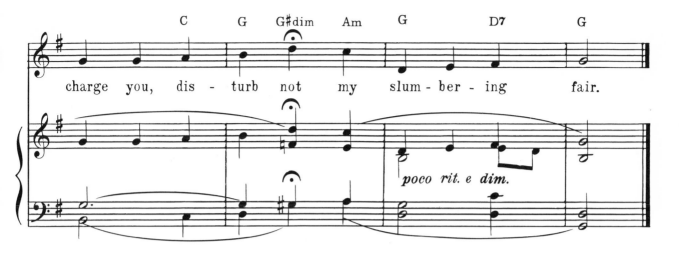

charge you, dis - turb not my slum - ber - ing fair.

poco rit. e dim.

Flow gently, sweet Afton, amang thy green braes,
Flow gently, I'll sing thee a song in thy praise;
My Mary's asleep by thy murmuring stream,
Flow gently, sweet Afton, disturb not her dream.

Thou stock dove whose echo resounds thro' the
   glen,
Ye wild whistling blackbirds in yon thorny den,
Thou green crested lapwing thy screaming forbear,
I charge you, disturb not my slumbering fair.

How lofty, sweet Afton, thy neighboring hills,
Far mark'd with the courses of clear, winding rills;
There daily I wander as noon rises high,
My flocks and my Mary's sweet cot in my eye.

How pleasant thy banks and green valleys below,
Where, wild in the woodlands, the primroses blow;
There oft, as mild evening weeps over the lea,
The sweet-scented birk shades my Mary and me.

Thy crystal stream, Afton, how lovely it glides,
And winds by the cot where my Mary resides;
How wanton thy waters her snowy feet lave,
As, gathering sweet flowerets, she stems thy clear
   wave.

Flow gently, sweet Afton, amang thy green braes,
Flow gently, sweet river, the theme of my lays;
My Mary's asleep by thy murmuring stream,
Flow gently, sweet Afton, disturb not her dream.

birk: birch.

The Blue Bells of Scotland

This is supposed to have been composed and sung by a Mrs. Jordon, a famous London actress, who recorded it as her own handiwork in 1800. It is sometimes listed as an English song.

Oh where, tell me where is your_ High land lad-die gone? Oh

where, tell me where is your_ High-land lad-die gone? He's

gone wi' stream-ing ban-ners where_ no-ble deeds are done, And it's

138

oh, in my heart I_____ wish him safe at home.

Oh where, tell me where is your Highland laddie
  gone?
Oh where, tell me where is your Highland laddie
  gone?
He's gone with streaming banners where noble
  deeds are done,
And it's oh, in my heart I wish him safe at home.

Oh where, tell me where did your Highland laddie
  dwell?
Oh where, tell me where did your Highland laddie
  dwell?
He dwelt in bonnie Scotland, where blooms the
  sweet blue bell,
And it's oh, in my heart I lo'e my laddie well.

Oh what, tell me what does your Highland laddie
  wear?
Oh what, tell me what does your Highland laddie
  wear?
A bonnet with a lofty plume, and on his breast a
  plaid,
And it's oh, in my heart I lo'e my Highland lad.

Oh what, tell me what if your Highland lad be
  slain?
Oh what, tell me what if your Highland lad be
  slain?
Oh, no, true love will be his guard and bring him
  safe again,
For it's oh, my heart would break if my Highland
  lad were slain!

Baloo Baleerie

The source of this lovely lullaby is unknown; it is
presumed to be a translation from the Gaelic.

Lento

Ba - loo ba - lee - rie, ba - loo ba -
lee - rie, ba - loo ba - lee - rie, Ba - loo ba - lee.

Gang a - wa' pee - rie fair - ies, Gang a - wa' pee - rie

p molto espress.

rit. e dim.

mp a tempo

140

fair - ies, Gang a - wa' pee - rie fair - ies Frae oor ben noo.

rit. e dim.

Baloo baleerie, baloo baleerie, baloo baleerie,
Baloo balee.

    Gang awa' peerie fairies,
    Gang awa' peerie fairies,
    Gang awa' peerie fairies
    Frae oor ben noo.
    Chorus:

    Doun come the bonny angels,
    Doun come the bonny angels,
    Doun come the bonny angels
    Tae oor ben noo.
    Chorus:

    Sleep saft my baby,
    Sleep saft my baby,
    Sleep saft my baby
    In oor ben noo.
    Chorus:

peerie: very small. *ben:* an inner room.

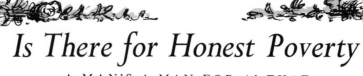

Is There for Honest Poverty

A MAN'S A MAN FOR A' THAT

ROBERT BURNS

Also known as "A Man's a Man for A' That," this incendiary celebration of the workingman has long been a favorite of labor and the left in English-speaking countries.

Allegretto

Is there for hon-est pov-er-ty That hangs his head an' a' that; The

cow-ard slave, we pass him by, We dare be poor for a' that! For

a'___ that, an' a'___ that, Our toils ob-scure an' a' that, The

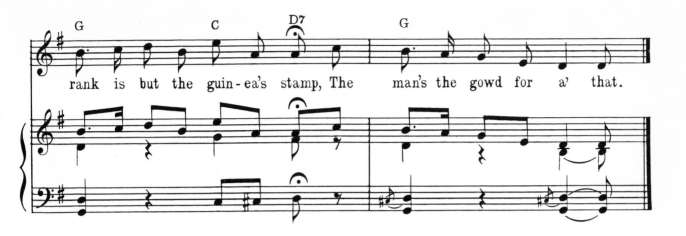

rank is but the guin-ea's stamp, The man's the gowd for a' that.

Is there for honest poverty
  That hangs his head, an' a' that;
The coward slave—we pass him by,
  We dare be poor for a' that!
For a' that, an' a' that,
  Our toils obscure an' a' that,
The rank is but the guinea's stamp,
  The man's the gowd for a' that.

What though on hamely fare we dine,
  Wear hoddin grey, an' a' that?
Gie fools their silks, and knaves their wine,
  A man's a man for a' that.
For a' that, an' a' that,
  Their tinsel show an' a' that,
The honest man, tho' e'er sae poor,
  Is king o' men for a' that.

Ye see yon birkie ca'd a lord,
  Wha struts, an' stares, an' a' that;
Tho' hundreds worship at his word,
  He's but a coof for a' that,
For a' that, an' a' that,
  His ribband, star, an' a' that,
The man o' independent mind
  He looks an' laughs at a' that.

A prince can mak a belted knight,
  A marquis, duke, an' a' that;
But an honest man's aboon his might,
  Gude faith, he maunna fa' that!
For a' that, an' a' that,
  Their dignities an' a' that,
The pith o' sense, an' pride o' worth,
  Are higher rank than a' that.

Then let us pray that come it may,
  (As come it will for a' that),
That Sense and Worth, o'er a' the earth,
  Shall bear the gree, an' a' that.
For a' that, an' a' that,
  It's coming yet for a' that,
That man to man, the world o'er,
  Shall brithers be for a' that.

hoddin grey: cloth the natural color of the wool. *birkie:* boastful fellow. *coof:* fool. *maunna fa' that:* cannot claim that.
bear the gree: come first.

Corn Rigs Are Bonnie

ROBERT BURNS

A charming song of seduction recollected in tranquillity, which Burns set to a tune from *Playford's Choice Ayres* (1681). It should be sung fairly fast, with a flowing rhythm.

Moderato

It was up-on a Lam mas night, When corn rigs are bon - nie, Be-neath the moon's un - cloud-ed light, I held a-wa to An - nie: The time flew by, wi'

tent - less _ heed, Till, 'tween the _ late _ and _ ear - ly; Wi'

sma' per-sua - sion _ she _ a - greed, To see _ me thro' the _

rit.   *a tempo*

bar - ley. Corn _ rigs, an' _ bar - ley _ rigs,

Chorus

rit. e dim.   *mf a tempo*

Corn _ rigs _ are _ bon - nie; I'll ne'er for-get _ that _

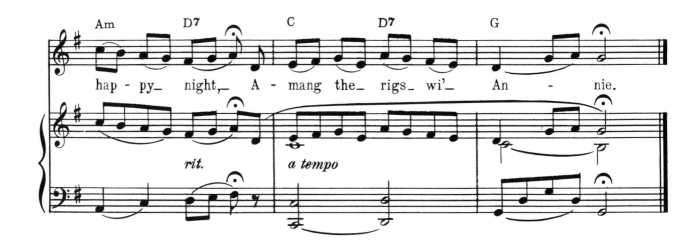

hap- py_ night,_ A - mang the_ rigs_ wi'_ An - nie.

rit. *a tempo*

It was upon a Lammas night,
    When corn rigs are bonnie,
Beneath the moon's unclouded light,
    I held awa to Annie:
The time flew by, wi' tentless heed,
    Till, 'tween the late and early;
Wi' sma' persuasion she agreed,
    To see me thro' the barley.

Corn rigs, an' barley rigs,
    Corn rigs are bonnie:
I'll ne'er forget that happy night,
    Amang the rigs wi' Annie.

The sky was blue, the wind was still,
    The moon was shining clearly;
I set her down, wi' right good will,
    Amang the rigs o' barley:
I ken't her heart was a' my ain;
    I lov'd her most sincerely;
I kiss'd her owre and owre again,
    Amang the rigs o' barley.
Chorus:

I lock' her in my fond embrace;
    Her heart was beating rarely:
My blessings on that happy place,
    Amang the rigs o' barley!
But by the moon and stars so bright,
    That shone that hour so clearly!
She ay shall bless that happy night,
    Amang the rigs o' barley.
Chorus:

I hae been blythe wi' comrades dear;
    I hae been merry drinking;
I hae been joyfu' gath'rin gear;
    I hae been happy thinking:
But a' the pleasures e'er I saw,
    Tho' three times doubl'd fairly,
That happy night was worth them a',
Amang the rigs o' barley.
Chorus:

146   *Lammas night:* a harvest festival celebrated August 1.   *rigs:* ridges.   *tentless:* careless.   *gath'rin gear:* money-making.

Can Ye Sew Cushions?

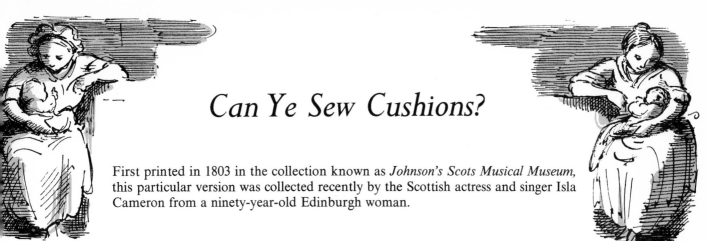

First printed in 1803 in the collection known as *Johnson's Scots Musical Museum*, this particular version was collected recently by the Scottish actress and singer Isla Cameron from a ninety-year-old Edinburgh woman.

O can ye sew cush-ions? and can ye sew sheets? And can ye sing ba-la-loo, when the bairn greets? And hee and baw bird-ie, hee and baw lamb,

O can ye sew cushions? and can ye sew sheets?
And can ye sing ba-la-loo, when the bairn greets?

And hee and baw birdie, hee and baw lamb,
Hee and baw birdie, my bonnie wee lamb.
Hee O, wee O, what would I do wi' you?
Black's the life that I lead wi' you!
Mony o' you, little for to gie you;
Hee O, wee O, what would I do wi' you?

I biggit the cradle all on the tree top
And the wind it did blaw, and the cradle did rock.
Chorus:

Now hush-a-ba, lammie, and hush-a-ba, dear,
Now hush-a-ba lammie, thy minnie is here.
Chorus:

The wild wind is ravin', thy minnie's heart's sair;
The wild wind is ravin', and you dinna care.
Chorus:

Sing ba-la-loo, lammie, sing ba-la-loo, dear,
Does the wee lammie ken that his daddie's no here?
Chorus:

Ye're rockin' fu' sweetly upon my warm knee,
But your daddie's a-rockin' upon the saut sea.
Chorus:

minnie: mother.   *biggit:* built.

A Highland Lad My Love Was Born

ROBERT BURNS

Set to an early dance tune known as "The White Cockade," this is usually played and sung in fast tempo, although it is much more effective when performed poignantly and slowly. "Highland" should be pronounced "Hieland."

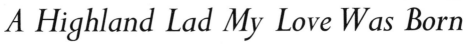

Andante espressivo

A— High-land lad my— love was born, The Law-land laws— he—
held in scorn; But he still was faith-fu'— to his clan, My—
gal-lant— braw— John— High-land-man. Sing— hey, my braw John

molto rit.

allargando

150

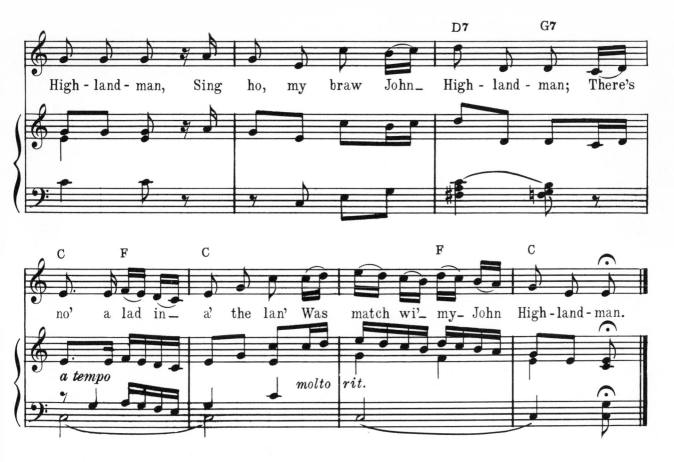

High-land-man, Sing ho, my braw John_ High-land-man; There's

no' a lad in_ a' the lan' Was match wi' my_ John High-land-man.

A Highland lad my love was born,
   The Lawland laws he held in scorn;
But he still was faithful to his clan,
   My gallant braw John Highlandman.
     Sing hey, my braw John Highlandman,
     Sing ho, my braw John Highlandman;
     There's no' a lad in a' the lan'
     Was match wi' my John Highlandman.

With his philabeg and tartan plaid,
And gude claymore doun by his side;
The ladies' hearts he did trepan——
My gallant braw John Highlandman.
     Sing hey, my braw John Highlandman,
     Sing ho, my braw John Highlandman;
     There's no' a lad in a' the lan'
     Was match wi' my John Highlandman.

They banish'd him beyond the sea;
But ere the bud was on the tree,
Adoun my cheeks the pearls they ran,
Embracing my John Highlandman.
     Sing hey, my braw John Highlandman,
     Sing ho, my braw John Highlandman;
     There's no' a lad in a' the lan'
     Was match wi' my John Highlandman.

philabeg: *kilt.* claymore: *two-handed sword.*

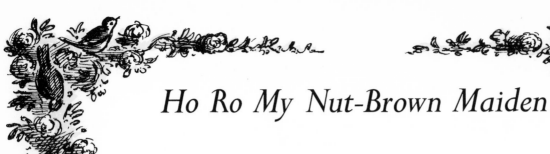

Ho Ro My Nut-Brown Maiden

One of the most popular songs of the Highlands, this was translated from the Gaelic in the late nineteenth century by the Scottish poet John Stuart Blackie.

Ho ro my nut-brown maid - en, Hee ree my nut-brown maid - en, Ho

ro__ ro__ maid - en, For she's the maid for me.

poco rit. e dim.

Her__ eye so mild-ly beam-ing, Her look so frank and free, In__

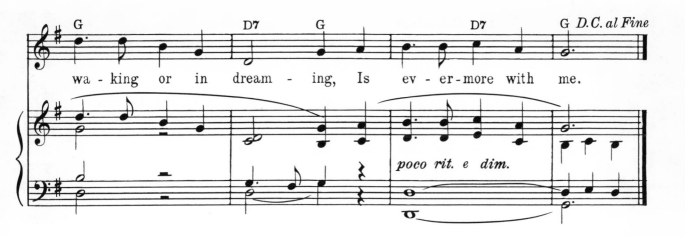

wa - king   or   in   dream - ing,   Is   ev - er - more   with   me.

Ho ro my nut-brown maiden,
Hee ree my nut-brown maiden,
Ho ro ro maiden,
For she's the maid for me.

Her eye so mildly beaming,
  Her look so frank and free,
In waking or in dreaming,
  Is evermore with me.
Chorus:

O Mary, mild-eyed Mary,
  By land or on the sea;
Though time or tide may vary
  My heart beats true for thee.
Chorus:

And since from thee I parted,
  A long and weary while;
I wander heavy hearted
  With longing for thy smile.
Chorus:

Mine eyes that never vary
  From pointing to the glen,
Where blooms my Highland Mary
  Like wild rose 'neath the ben.
Chorus:

And when with blossoms laden
  Bright summer comes again;
I'll fetch my nut-brown maiden
  Down from the bonnie glen.
Chorus:

Robin Adair

LADY CAROLINE KEPPEL

These lyrics, sometimes ascribed to Robert Burns, are by Lady Caroline Keppel, who reputedly married an Irish surgeon, Robin Adair, in 1758. She fitted the words to an ancient Irish air (fourteenth century) that he had sung to her. The melody as sung in England is slightly different.

Andante

What's this dull town to me? Rob - in's not near.

What was't I wish'd to see, What wish'd to hear?

Where all the joy and mirth made this_ town_ heav'n on earth?

Oh, they're all — fled with thee, Rob-in A-dair.

What's this dull town to me?
  Robin's not near.
What was't I wish'd to see,
  What wish'd to hear?
Where all the joy and mirth
Made this town heav'n on earth?
Oh, they're all fled with thee,
  Robin Adair.

What made th' assembly shine?
  Robin Adair.
What made the ball so fine?
  Robin was there.
What when the play was o'er,
What made my heart so sore?
Oh, it was parting with
  Robin Adair.

But now thou'rt cold to me,
  Robin Adair.
But now thou'rt cold to me,
  Robin Adair.
Yet he I lov'd so well
Still in my heart shall dwell;
Oh, I can ne'er forget
  Robin Adair.

Awa', Whigs, Awa'

The Whigs, named after the rebels who marched on Edinburgh in 1648, had become by the late eighteenth century the party of large landowners and wealthy merchants. This song is partially by Robert Burns, partially (especially the chorus) from tradition. A verse about Bonnie Prince Charlie, written by James Hogg in the early nineteenth century, is sometimes added to the song: "I ance had sons but now hae nane;/ I bred them toiling sairly;/ And I wad bear them a' again/ And lose them a' for Charlie."

Animato e risoluto

A - wa' Whigs a - wa' A - wa' Whigs a - wa' Ye're but a pack o' trait - or loons Ye'll do nae gude at a'. Our thrist - les flour - ish'd fresh and fair, And bon - nie bloom'd our ros - es, But

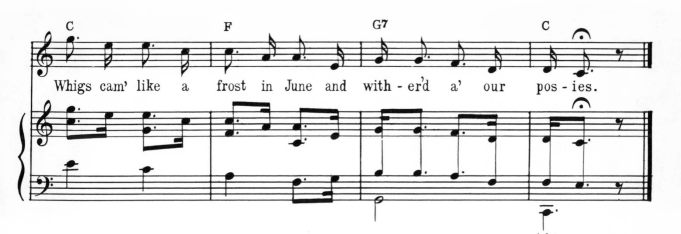

Whigs cam' like a frost in June and with-er'd a' our pos-ies.

Awa', Whigs, awa'!
 Awa', Whigs, awa!
Ye're but a pack o' traitor loons,
 Ye'll do nae gude at a'.

Our thristles flourished fresh and fair,
  And bonnie bloomed our roses,
But Whigs cam' like a frost in June,
  And wither'd a' our posies.
Chorus:

Our ancient crown's fa'n in the dust——
  Deil blin' them wi' the stoure o't;
And write their names in his black beuk
  Wha gae the Whigs the power o't!
Chorus:

Our sad decay in Church or State
  Surpasses my describing;
The Whigs cam' o'er us for a curse,
  And we hae done wi' thriving.
Chorus:

Grim vengeance lang has ta'en a nap,
  But we may see him wauken;
Gude help the day when royal heads
  Are hunted like a maukin!
Chorus:

deil: devil. *stoure:* rising dust. *wauken:* watching. *maukin:* a hare.

My Luve Is Like a Red, Red Rose

ROBERT BURNS

This beautiful love song is set to a tune Burns found in *Oswald's Companion Book,* published in 1745.

Andante

1. O, my luve is like a red, red rose, that's new-ly sprung in June; O, my
2. Till— a' the seas gang dry, my dear, till a' the seas gang dry; And—

luve is like a mel - o - die that's sweet-ly played in tune!
I will luve thee still, my dear, till a' the seas gang dry.

As fair art thou, my bon - nie lass, so deep in luve am I— And—

I will luve thee still, my dear, till a' the seas gang dry.

O, my luve is like a red, red rose, that's newly sprung in June;
O, my luve is like a melodie that's sweetly played in tune!
As fair art thou, my bonnie lass, so deep in luve am I;
And I will luve thee still, my dear, till a' the seas gang dry.
Till a' the seas gang dry, my dear, till a' the seas gang dry;
And I will luve thee still, my dear, till a' the seas gang dry.

Till a' the seas gang dry, my dear, and the rocks melt wi' the sun;
And I will luve thee still, my dear, while the sands of life shall run.
But, fare thee weel, my only luve! O fare thee weel awhile!
And I will come again, my luve, tho' 'twere ten thousand mile.
Tho' 'twere ten thousand mile, my luve, tho' 'twere ten thousand mile,
And I will come again, my luve, tho' 'twere ten thousand mile.

Weaving Lilt

One of the finest collections of folk songs is *Songs of the Hebrides,* collected, edited, and translated by Marjory Kennedy-Fraser and Kenneth Macleod, and published in 1917. This particular song from that collection is still sung in Gaelic by the island women at their work.

Moderato

Wait to-day, love, till___ to-mor - row, Ho - ro e - ci-can a - rin hu - o, While I weave fine lin-en for thee, love, Lin-en for thee, fine lin-en for thee, love, While___ I weave fine

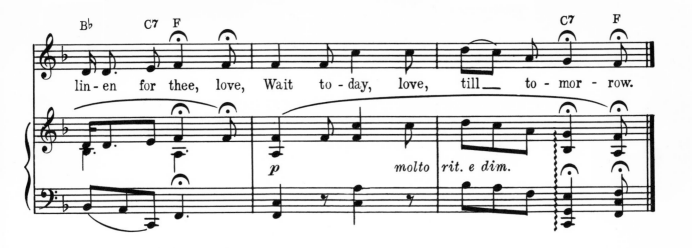

lin - en for thee, love, Wait to - day, love, till___ to - mor - row.

p   *molto rit. e dim.*

Wait today, love, till tomorrow,
Horo ecican arin huo.
While I weave fine linen for thee, love,
Linen for thee, fine linen for thee, love,
While I weave fine linen for thee, love,
Wait today, love, till tomorrow.

Wait today until tomorrow.
Horo ecican arin huo.
Sown is the lint, but och, will it grow, love?
Linen for thee, fine linen for thee, love,
Sure will it grow fine linen for thee, love?
Wait today, love, till tomorrow.

Shuttle I lent to the King of France, love,
Horo ecican arin huo.
Loom, it grows in the wood of St. Patrick,
Shuttle, nor loom, nor lint, nor loom,
Nor shuttle, nor loom, have I to weave,
Nor lint, nor loom, nor shuttle, nor loom,
Yet wait till I weave fine linen for thee, love.
Wait today until tomorrow.

horo ecican arin huo: pronounced "ho-ro aitch-e-can ah-rin hu-o."

Skye Boat Song

SIR HAROLD BOULTON   ANNIE MacLEOD

The most familiar of the many songs about Bonnie Prince Charlie, this celebrates
his escape from the Scotch mainland to the island of Skye after his defeat at the
Battle of Culloden Moor in 1745. The "Flora" referred to was a Jacobite patriot,
Flora MacDonald, who helped him escape.

Andante con moto

"Speed, bon-nie boat, like a bird on the wing, On-ward," the sail-ors cry!

"Car-ry the lad that's born to be king, O-ver the sea to Skye!"

Loud the winds howl, loud the waves roar, Thun-der clouds rend the air;

Baf-fled our foes stand on the shore, Fol-low they will not dare.—

"Speed, bonnie boat, like a bird on the wing,
Onward," the sailors cry!
"Carry the lad that's born to be king,
Over the sea to Skye!"

Loud the winds howl, loud the waves roar,
  Thunder clouds rend the air;
Baffled our foes stand on the shore,
  Follow they will not dare.
Chorus:

Though the waves leap, soft shall ye sleep,
  Ocean's a royal bed;
Rock'd in the deep, Flora will keep
  Watch by your weary head.
Chorus:

Many's the lad fought on that day,
  Well the claymore could wield,
When the night came, silently lay
  Dead on Culloden's field.
Chorus:

Burn'd are our homes, exile and death
  Scatter the loyal men;
Yet, e'er the sword cool in the sheath,
  Charlie will come again.
Chorus:

To the Beggin' I Will Go

Identified with the Aberdeen tinkers, this song celebrates the free and unfettered gypsy life in much the same fashion as the American "bum" song, "The Big Rock-Candy Mountain," and has similarities in feeling with the famous English ballad, "The Wraggle-Taggle Gipsies."

If the beg-gin' be as good a trade As I have heard them say, It's time that I was on the road And jog-gin' doon the brae, To the beg-gin' I will go, will go, To the beg-gin' I will go.

If the beggin' be as good a trade
    As I have heard them say,
It's time that I was on the road
    And joggin' doon the brae,
To the beggin' I will go, will go,
    To the beggin' I will go.

And if a' the time we'll gang awa'
    I'll let my hair grow lang,
I will not pare my nails at a'
    For the beggars wear them lang,
To the beggin' I will go, will go,
    To the beggin' I will go.

I'll gang to the tailors,
    They call him Arnie Gray;
I'll gat him mak' a coat to me
    That will help me night and day,
To the beggin' I will go, will go,
    To the beggin' I will go.

And if there be a weddin'
    And me chance to be there;
I'll rise amang the weddin' folk
    And bless the happy pair,
To the beggin' I will go, will go,
    To the beggin' I will go.

It's some'll give me beef and breed,
    And some'll give me cheese,
And out amang the weddin' folk
    I'll gather bawbees,
To the beggin' I will go, will go,
    To the beggin' I will go.

And if a' come on as weel's a' like
    It's I'll come back and tell;
But gin a gin a dae that
    I'll keep it to mysel',
To the beggin' I will go, will go,
    To the beggin' I will go.

bawbees: half pennies.
gin a gin a dae that: if it doesn't do that.

Ye Banks and Braes o' Bonnie Doon

ROBERT BURNS

The melody to this is purported to have been written in 1788 by a Charles Miller, who expressed a desire to compose "an authentic Scots air," and was advised by a friend, partly in jest, to "keep to the black keys of the harpsicord and maintain some kind of rhythm." This he did, and we are all forever grateful.

Ye banks and braes o' bon-nie Doon, How can ye bloom sae fresh and fair? How can ye chant, ye lit-tle birds, And I sae wear-y, fu' o' care! Ye'll break my heart, ye

Ye banks and braes o' bonnie Doon,
  How can ye bloom sae fresh and fair?
How can ye chant, ye little birds,
  And I'm sae weary, fu' o' care!
Ye'll break my heart, ye warbling bird,
  That wantons through the flow'ring thorn,
Ye mind me o' departed joys,
  Departed never to return.

Oft ha'e I roved by bonnie Doon,
  To see the rose and woodbine twine;
And ilka bird sang o' its luve,
  And fondly sae did I o' mine.
Wi' lightsome heart I stretch'd my hand,
  And pu'd a rosebud from the tree;
But my fause lover stole the rose,
  And left, and left the thorn wi' me.

Scots Wha Ha'e wi' Wallace Bled

ROBERT BURNS

James Currie's edition of the songs of Robert Burns (1800) gives this song the title, "Bruce to His Troops on the Eve of the Battle of Bannockburn." This battle, in 1314, was a celebrated victory for the Scottish forces, led by Robert Bruce, who totally defeated the troops of King Edward II. The song has since become the unofficial Scottish national anthem. "Wallace" was Sir William Wallace, who died in 1305, and who was known as "the Hammer and Scourge of England."

Con spirito

Scots, wha ha'e wi' Wal-lace bled! Scots, wham Bruce has af-ten led!

Wel-come to your gor-y bed, Or to vic - to - ry!

Now's the day and now's the hour; See the front of bat-tle lour!

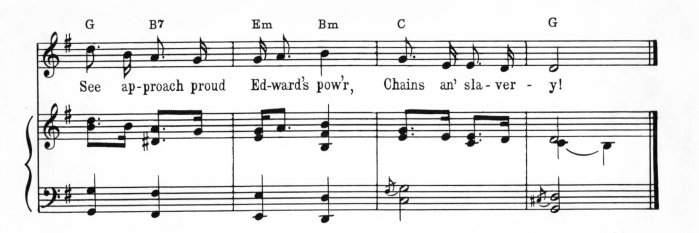

See ap-proach proud Ed-ward's pow'r, Chains an' sla-ver - y!

Scots, wha ha'e wi' Wallace bled!
Scots, wham Bruce has aften led!
Welcome to your gory bed,
   Or to victory!
Now's the day and now's the hour;
See the front of battle lour!
See approach proud Edward's pow'r,
   Chains and slavery!

Wha would be a traitor knave?
Wha will fill a coward's grave?
Wha sae base as be a slave?
   Let him turn an' flee!

Wha, for Scotland's king an' law,
Freedom's sword would strongly draw,
Freeman stand, and freeman fa',
   Let him on wi' me!

By oppression's woes an' pains,
By your sons in servile chains,
We will drain our dearest veins,
   But they shall be free.
Lay the proud usurpers low!
Tyrants fall in every foe!
Liberty's in every blow!
   Let us do or dee!

Charlie Is My Darling

One of the most popular songs from the Jacobite Rebellion, these lyrics have been variously attributed to James Hogg and Lady Carolina Nairne. An earlier version celebrates Bonnie Prince Charlie as a ladies' man. The music is traditional.

Oh! Char - lie is my dar - ling, my dar - ling my dar - ling! Oh! Char - lie is my dar - ling, the young che - va - lier.

'Twas on a Mon - day morn - ing, Right ear - ly in the year, When

Char-lie came to our town, The young che-va-lier. Oh! Char-lie is my dar-ling, my dar-ling, my dar-ling! Oh, Char-lie is my dar-ling, the young che-va-lier.

Oh! Charlie is my darling, my darling, my darling!
Oh! Charlie is my darling, the young chevalier.

'Twas on a Monday morning,
Right early in the year,
When Charlie came to our town,
The young chevalier.
Chorus:

As he cam' marchin' up the street,
The pipes played loud and clear;
And a' the folk cam' rinnin' out
To meet the chevalier.
Chorus:

Wi' Highland bonnets on their heads,
And claymores bright and clear,
They cam' to fight for Scotland's right,
And the young chevalier.
Chorus:

They've left their bonnie Highland hills,
Their wives and bairnies dear,
To draw the sword for Scotland's lord,
The young chevalier.
Chorus:

Oh! there were mony beating hearts,
And mony a hope and fear;
And mony were the pray'rs put up
For the young chevalier.
Chorus:

claymore: two-handed sword.

Oh Rowan Tree

LADY CAROLINA NAIRNE

From R. A. Smith's collection, *Scottish Minstrel*, published in 1822. A rowan is a European mountain ash.

Oh— row-an tree, oh row-an tree, thou'lt aye be dear to me,— Entwin'd thou art wi' mo-ny ties, o' hame and in-fan-cy. Thy
leaves were aye the first of spring, thy flow'rs the sim-mer's pride;— There

was nae sic a bon-nie tree, in all the coun-try side. Oh— row — an tree!

Oh rowan tree, oh rowan tree, thoul't aye be dear to me,
   Entwin'd thou art wi' mony ties, o' hame and infancy.
Thy leaves were aye the first o' spring, thy flowr's the simmer's pride;
   There was nae sic a bonnie tree, in all the country side.
Oh rowan tree.

How fair wert thou in simmer time, wi' all thy clusters white,
   How rich and gay thy autumn dress, wi' berries red and bright.
On thy fair stem were mony names which now nae mair I see,
   But there engraven on my heart, forgot they ne'er can be.
Oh rowan tree.

We sat aneath thy spreading shade, the bairnies round thee ran,
   They pu'd thy bonnie berries red and necklaces they strang.
My mither oh, I see her still, she smil'd our sports to see,
   Wi' little Jeannie on her lap, wi' Jamie at her knee.
Oh rowan tree.

Oh, there arose my father's pray'r in holy evening's calm,
   How sweet was then my mither's voice in the martyr's psalm;
Now a' are gane! we meet nae mair aneath the rowan tree,
   But hallowed thoughts around thee twine o' hame and infancy.
Oh rowan tree.

Will Ye No' Come Back Again?

According to Ewan MacColl this is the most popular of all the "Bonnie Prince Charlie songs" in Scotland today. It is used as a parting song for all occasions.

Andante

Bon-nie Char-lie's now a-wa, Safe-ly owre the friend-ly main;

Mon-y a heart will break in twa, Should he no' come back a-gain.

Chorus

Will ye no' come back a-gain? Will ye no' come back a-gain?

Bet-ter lo'ed ye can-na be, Will ye no' come back a-gain?

p a tempo

molto espress. e rit.

Bonnie Charlie's now awa',
Safely owre the friendly main;
Mony a heart will break in twa,
Should he no' come back again.

Will ye no' come back again?
Will ye no' come back again?
Better lo'ed ye canna be,
Will ye no' come back again?

Mony a traitor 'mang the isles
Brak the band o' nature's laws;
Mony a traitor wi' his wiles,
Sought to wear his life awa'.
Chorus:

Whene'er I hear the blackbird sing,
Unto the evening sinking down,
Or merl that makes the woods to ring,
To me they hae nae other sound.
Chorus:

Mony a gallant sodger faught,
Mony a gallant chief did fa',
Death itself were dearly bought,
A' for Scotland's king and law.
Chorus:

Sweet the lav'rock's note and lang,
Lilting wildly up the glen;
And aye the o'erword o' the sang,
"Will he no' come back again?"
Chorus:

The Piper o' Dundee

A song from the Jacobite Rebellion of 1745, full of long-forgotten references. The men mentioned in the text were Jacobite leaders; Amulrie is a remote village in Perthshire where they held secret meetings.

Chorus-Moderato

The pip-er came to our town, To our town, to our town, The pip-er came to our town, And he played bon-nie - lie.

Verse

He play'd a spring, the laird to please, A spring brent new frae 'yont the seas, And

then he gae his bags a wheeze And play'd a-nith-er key.

D.C. al Fine

The piper came to our town,
To our town, to our town,
The piper came to our town,
And he played bonnielie.
He play'd a spring, the laird to please,
A spring brent new frae 'yont the seas,
And then he gae his bags a wheeze
And play'd anither key.

And wasna he a roguey,
A roguey, a roguey?
And wasna he a roguey,
The piper o' Dundee?

He play'd "The Welcome Ower the Main,"
And "Ye's Be Fou and I'se Be Fain,"
And "Auld Stuart's Back Again,"
Wi' muckle mirth and glee.
He play'd "The Kirk," he play'd "The Queer,"
"The Mullin Dhu," and "Chevalier,"
And "Lang Awa' But Welcome Here,"
Sae sweet, sae bonnielie.
Chorus:

It's some gat swords and some gat nane,
And some were dancing mad their lane,
And mony a vow o' weir was ta'en
That night at Amulrie
There was Tullibardine and Burleigh,
And Struan, Keith and Ogilvie,
And brave Carnegie, wha' but he,
The piper o' Dundee.
Chorus:

spring: dance.   brent new: brand new.   *"Ye's Be Fou and I'se Be Fain":* you're drunk, and I'm willing.   muckle: much.   *"The Queer":*
the choir.   *gat:* have.   *mad their lane:* by themselves.   *weir:* war.

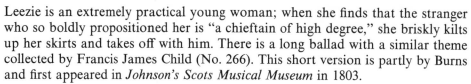

Leezie Lindsay

Leezie is an extremely practical young woman; when she finds that the stranger who so boldly propositioned her is "a chieftain of high degree," she briskly kilts up her skirts and takes off with him. There is a long ballad with a similar theme collected by Francis James Child (No. 266). This short version is partly by Burns and first appeared in *Johnson's Scots Musical Museum* in 1803.

Allegretto

"Will ye gang tae the Hie-lands, Lee-zie Lind-say? Will ye gang tae the Hie-lands wi' me? Will ye gang tae the Hie-lands, Lee-zie Lind-say, My

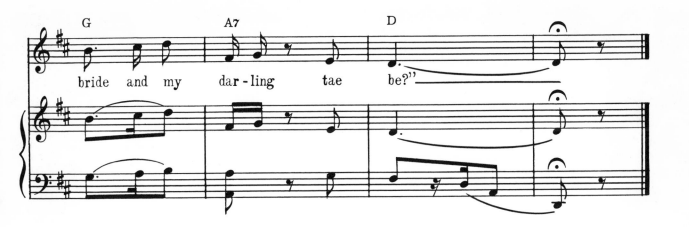

"Will ye gang tae the Hielands, Leezie Lindsay?
Will ye gang tae the Hielands wi' me?
Will ye gang tae the Hielands, Leezie Lindsay,
My bride and my darling tae be?"

"To gang to the Hielands wi' you, sir,
I dinna ken how that may be;
For I ken nae the land that ye live in,
Nor ken I the lad I'm gaun wi'."

"O, Leezie, lass, ye maun ken little,
If sae be ye dinna ken me;
For my name is Lord Ronald MacDonald,
A chieftain o' high degree."

She has kilted her coats o' green satin,
She has kilted them up tae her knee,
Ans she's aff wi' Lord Ronald MacDonald
His bride and his darling tae be.

The Road to the Isles

The best known of the *Songs of the Hebrides,* it is almost impossible to sing this without tapping your foot or beating time.

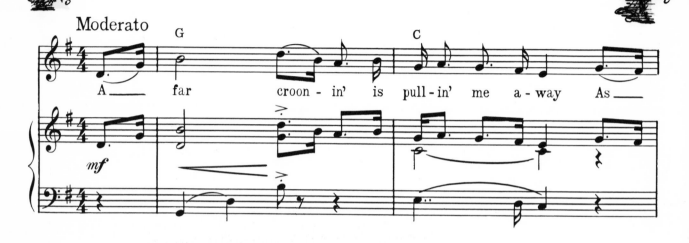

A ___ far croon-in' is pull-in' me a-way As ___

take I wi' my cro-mack to the road. The _ far Coo-lins are

put-tin' love on me As step I with the sun-light for my load. _____ Sure by

Tum-mel and Loch Ran-noch and Loch-a-ber I will go, By heath-er tracks wi' heav-en in their wiles; If it's think-in' in your in-ner heart the brag-gart's in my step, You've nev-er smelled the tan-gle o' the Isles. Oh the far Coo - lins are put-tin' love on me As step I wi' my cro-mack to the Isles.

A far croonin' is pullin' me away
As take I wi' my cromack to the road.
The far Coolins are puttin' love on me
As step I with the sunlight for my load.

Sure by Tummel and Loch Rannoch and Lochaber
*   I will go,*
By heather tracks wi' heaven in their wiles;
If it's thinkin' in your inner heart the braggart's in
*   my step,*
You've never smelled the tangle o' the Isles.
The far Coolins are puttin' love on me
As step I wi' my cromack to the Isles.

It's by Shiel water the track is to the west,
By Aillort and by Morar to the sea.
The cool cresses I am thinkin' of for pluck
And bracken for a wink on Mother knee.
Chorus:

The blue islands are pullin' me away,
Their laughter puts the leap upon the lame;
The blue islands from the Skerries to the Lewis,
Wi' heather honey taste upon each name.
Chorus:

182   *cromack:* walking stick with crooked handle.   *Coolins:* Skye mountains.   *Aillort:* pronounced "Aisle-ort."   *Lewis:* pronounced "Lews."

An Eriskay Love Lilt

Also known as "When I'm Lonely, Dear White Heart," this simple and haunting love song is one of the *Songs of the Hebrides*.

Lento

Vair me o, _____ ro van o, Vair me o, _____ ro van ee, Vair me o ru o__ ho Sad am I with-out thee.

poco rit. e dim.

Vair me o, ro van o,
Vair me o, ro van ee,
Vair me o ru o ho
Sad am I without thee.

When I'm lonely, dear white heart,
Black the night and wild the sea;
By love's light my foot finds
The old pathway to thee.
Chorus:

Thou'rt the music of my heart,
Harp of joy, o cruit mo chridh,
Moon of guidance by night,
Strength and light thou'rt to me.
Chorus:

cruit mo chridh: pronounced *crootch mo chree.*

The Songs of Wales

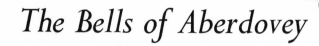

The Bells of Aberdovey

CLYCHAU ABERDYFI

English translation by Peter John Stephens

An old song, a caricatured version of which appeared in Charles Didben's play *Liberty Hall* in 1785. Brinley Richards, the Welsh folk-song scholar, remarks that "the more appropriate title would probably be 'The Bells of Abertawe,' (Swansea, South Wales)."

Moderato

If to me you can be true, Just as true as I to you, It's
Ohs oit tee un beer ee me,— Vel-roiv-vee un beer ee tee, Mahl

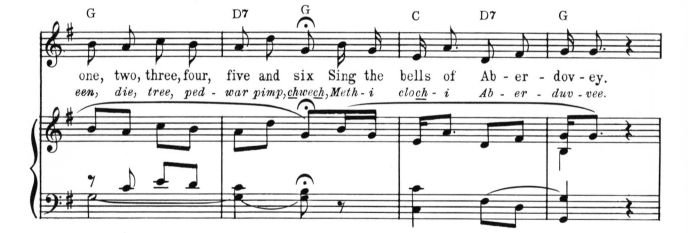

one, two, three, four, five and six Sing the bells of Ab-er-dov-ey.
een, die, tree, ped-war pimp, chwech, Meth-i cloch-i Ab-er-duv-vee.

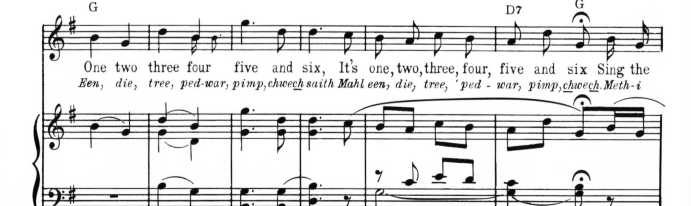

One two three four five and six, It's one, two, three, four, five and six Sing the
Een, die, tree, ped-war, pimp, chwech saith Mahl een, die, tree, 'ped-war, pimp, chwech. Meth-i

186

bells of Ab-er-dov-ey. Boys do love to be in love, And girls do love to
cloch - i Ab - er - duv-vee. *Huff gan vab you may thee sairch, Uh vairch my ahm bree-*

mar - ry. But my love's for on - ly one, For Bess of Ab-er-dov-ey.
od - ee, *Huff gan in - eye um hob man, On more-veeth Ab - er - duv - vee.*

If your love is just as true,— As this love I have for you, It's
Ohs oit teen vung har - ee - ee,—— *Vel roiv veen duh gar - ee - ee, Mahl*

187

one, two, three, four, five and six, From the bells of Ab - er - dov - ey.
een, die, tree, ped - war, pimp chwech, Meth-i clo*ch* - i Ab - er - duv - vee.

poco rit. e dim.

If to me you can be true,
Just as true as I to you,
It's one, two, three, four, five and six
Sing the bells of Aberdovey.
One, two, three, four, five and six,
It's one, two, three, four, five and six
Sing the bells of Aberdovey.
Boys do love to be in love,
And girls do love to marry.
But my love's for only one,
For Bess of Aberdovey.
If your love is just as true
As this love I have for you,
It's one, two, three, four, five and six,
From the bells of Aberdovey.

Bold with love I'm back once more
Just to camp against your door.
It's one, two, three, four, five and six,
Sing the bells of Aberdovey.
One, two, three, four, five and six,
It's one, two, three, four, five and six
Sing the bells of Aberdovey.
Here's an end to all faint hearts,
Till truce it is you're pleading.
If you just meet me half way,
It will be all I'm needing.
If your love is half as true
As this love I have for you,
It's one, two, three, four, five and six,
From the bells of Aberdovey.

Ohs oit tee un beer ee me,
Vel-roiv-vee un beer ee tee,
Mahl een, die, tree, ped-war, pimp, *chwech,*
Meth-i clo*ch*-i Ab-er-duv-vee.
Een, die, tree, ped-war, pimp, *chwech* saith
Mahl een, die, tree, ped-war, pimp, *chwech,*
Meth-i clo*ch*-i Ab-er-duv-vee.
Huff gan vab you may-thee sair*ch,*
Uh vair*ch* my ahm bree-od-ee,
Huff gan in-eye um hob man,
On more-veeth Ab-er-duv-vee.
Ohs oit teen vung har-ee-ee,
Vel roiv veen duh gar-ee-ee,
Mahl een, die, tree, ped-war, pimp, *chwech,*
Meth-i clo*ch*-i Ab-er-duv-vee.

Pan thove ad-rev tros uh more,
Cahr-yod gee-ra orth duh thor;
Mahl een, die, tree, ped-war, pimp, *chwech,*
Meth-i clo*ch*-i Ab-er-duv-vee.
Een, die, tree, ped-war, pimp, *chwech,* saith
Mahl een, die, tree, ped-war, pimp, *chwech,*
Meth-i clo*ch*-i Ab-er-duv-vee.
Pide i oo-nade un gol-on wahn,
Pan thou o dan-der vah-ner,
Ohs beeth gen it ire you thwoyd,
Beeth goon-oy dun we*ll* or han-ner.
Ohs oit teen vung har-ee-ee,
Vel roiv veen duh gar-ee-dee,
Mahl een, die, tree, ped-war, pimp, *chwech,*
Meth-i clo*ch*-i Ab-er-duv-vee.

ch: pronounced as in "Bach" or the Scotch "loch"
ll: pronounced by very rapidly saying the letters "tl" as if they were one sound, with a strong aspiration.

To See Swainson

HEFO DEIO I DYWYN

English lyrics by Llew Tegid

The Welsh words to this happy song (which are just as ridiculous as these) tell of an altogether different journey: "Going With Deio to Towyn."

Moderato

I re-ceived an in-vi-ta-tion Tra la la la la la la la
Me theer bun-yice boot-o luth-theer, Tra la la la la la la la

tra la la From a dear and old re-la-tion Tra la la la la la la la
Tra la la Athy oorth Mis-ter Jones o'er Breeth-deer Tra la la la la la la la

tra la la And I start-ed on the jour-ney Tra la la la la, tra
Tra la la Ok un hoon-noo roith un guv-vin Tra la la la la Tra

189

I received an invitation,
   Tra la la la la la la la, tra la la
From a dear and old relation,
   Tra la la la la la la la, tra la la la
And I started on the journey,
   Tra la la la la, tra la la la
To see Swainson down in Swansea
   Tra la la la la la, tra la la la la
Tra la la la la la la la, tra la la.

It was just the thing I'd relish, Tra la la, etc.
With my gloves and cane quite stylish, Tra la la, etc.
For I knew it would be jolly, Tra la la, etc.
To see Swainson down in Swansea, Tra la la, etc.

Everyone within the village,
Loudly praised my luck and courage,
To the station came to see me
Go to Swainson down in Swansea.

"Right away," and off we scamper,
Like a whirlwind in a temper,
It was bliss itself to fancy
Seeing Swainson down in Swansea.

Me theer-bun-yice boot-o luth-theer,
Tra la la la la la la la Tra la la
Athy-oorth Mister Jones o'er Breeth-deer,
Tra la la la la la la la Tra la la
Ok un hoon-noo roith un guv-vin
Tra la la la la Tra la la la
Ah'oon ee hev-vo Die-oy Duh-win.
Tra la la la la Tra la la la la
Tra la la la la la la la Tra la la

Beem un heer un sad ges eed-row, Tra la la etc.
Preen oith ora mind i pie-d'yo, Tra la la etc.
Ond wed-eer *oll* bee ee me gu*ch*-win, Tra la la etc.
Hev-vo die-yo ee foorth ee Duh-win, Tra la la etc.

Vay gu*ch*-win-wid ahr nos Wen-ner
Doe-ed ee vow'th-we air-been soo-pur
Vay guy'd un-no ee-oo'd uh men-in
Oorth vihnd hev-vo Die-yo Dow-win

Doe-ed um-line ok high-b'yore Deen-as
Uh *ch*aid bar-ah ah *ch*ouse ung wan-ahs
Troo'ee Dol-*ll*een eer ime un *ll*in-een
Oorth Vihnd hev-vo Die-yo Dow-win

190

Sudden stop—the door was opened,
I don't know howe'er it happened,
I was landed in Treorkey,
Ne'er saw Swainson, ne'er saw Swansea.

Doe-ed droo'ee Ab-er-eh-Gun-ol-win
Ok um-line don Greig-eh-Der-in
Pon ahr guv-ver En-es-mine-gwin
Gwaith-i Die-yo "Dok-oo Dow-win!"

ch: pronounced as in "Bach" or the Scotch "loch"
ll: pronounced by very rapidly saying the letters "tl" as if they were one sound, with a strong aspiration.

Robin Redbreast

ROBIN GOCH

English lyrics by Llew Tegid

This beautiful children's song, with its touching lyrics, is from Carnarvonshire.
The first verse is traditional, the remaining verses by Llew Tegid. It lends itself
particularly well to harmony.

Moderato

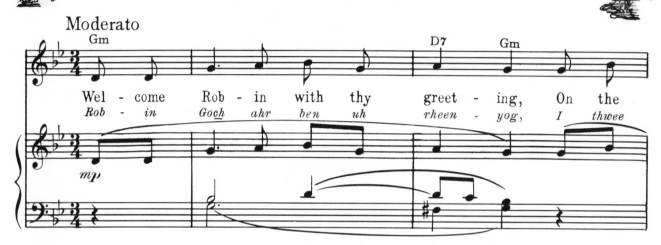

Wel - come Rob - in with thy greet - ing, On the
Rob - in Goch ahr ben uh rheen - yog, I thwee

thresh-old meek - ly wait - ing, To the chil-dren's home now en - ter, From the
uh den vach an oid - og; Ok un dwed-did un us mah - la My heen

cold and snow of win - ter, From the cold and snow of win - ter.
ower me thou un i - rah, My heen ower me thou un i - rah.

192

Welcome Robin with thy greeting,
On the threshold meekly waiting,
To the children's home now enter,
From the cold and snow of winter,
From the cold and snow of winter.

Art thou cold? or art thou hungry?
Pretty Robin, don't be angry,
All the children round thee rally,
While the snow is in the valley,
While the snow is in the valley.

Come in Robin, do not fear us,
Thy bright eye and chirping cheer us;
Thy sad notes excite our pity,
Now the frost begins to bite thee,
Now the frost begins to bite thee.

Robin, come and tell thy story,
Leave outside thy care and worry;
Tell the children, Robin dearest,
Of the babies in the forest,
Of the babies in the forest.

Of the flame that burnt thy bosom,
Of thy wand'rings far and lonesome,
Of thy home among the greenwood,
Of thy happy days of childhood,
Of thy happy days of childhood.

Robin Go*ch* ahr ben uh rheen-yog,
I-thwee uh den va*ch* an oid-og;
Ok un dwed-did un us mah-la
My heen ower me thou un i-rah,
My heen ower me thou un i-rah.

Robin Go*ch* seeth un neh-win-og,
Bron uh rheen-nee ahr uh rheen-yog,
Ok un dwed-did oorth uh mare-*ch*ed,
Ice-yo twee-mo, ice-yo tahm-med,
Ice-yo twee-mo, ice-yo tahm-med

Robin Go*ch* i goice-sigh min-yon,
Un uh roo i dry'd un oy-ree-yon,
Dwade i gwin bob hweer uh bore-rye,
My uh ree-oo un brath-ee mode-yi,
My uh ree-oo un brath-ee mode-yi.

Robin teer'd uh dwade duh han-ness,
Nee thou roo-oo ee gol-on gun-ness,
Teer'd eer coom-nee ak um-dwee-ma,
My heen o'er me thou un i-rah,
My heen o'er me thou un i-rah.

Robin Go*ch* more vween duh drud-dar,
Oit feeth-lon-av or ho*ll* ah-dar,
My uh guy-av o'er un goo-gee,
Tee guy lo*ch*-es um-i le*ch*-ee,
Tee guy lo*ch*-es um-i le*ch*-ee.

ch: pronounced as in "Bach" or the Scotch "loch"
ll: pronounced by very rapidly saying the letters "tl" as if they were one sound, with a strong aspiration.

David of the White Rock

DAFYDD Y GAREG WEN

Welsh lyrics by Ceriog   *English translation by Peter John Stephens*

An ancient song which first saw publication in *Relicks of the Welsh Bards* in 1794.
Tradition has it that a bard named David, on his deathbed, called for his harp and
composed this lovely melody, requesting that it be played at his funeral.

Bring me my harp was David's sad sigh,—
Car yuch meth Dah-veeth vun hail-een ee me,—

I would play one more tune before I die.
Kise-yahv kin mahr-oo-roy tone ahr nee he.

Help me, dear wife, put my hands to the strings
Code uch vuh noy-la-oo ee gur eith uh tant,—

"Bring me my harp," was David's sad sigh,
"I would play one more tune before I die.
Help me, dear wife, put the hands to the strings,
I wish my loved ones the blessing God brings."

"Last night an angel called with heaven's breath:
'David, play, and come through the gates of death!'
Farewell, faithful harp, farewell to your strings,
I wish my loved ones the blessing God brings."

Car-yu*ch* meth Dah-veeth vun hail-een ee me,
Kise-yahv kin mahr-oo roy tone ahr-nee he.
Code u*ch* vuh noy-la-oo ee gur-eith uh tant,
Dew a*ch* ben-deeth-yo vung weth-oo am plant.

Nithe your me gloo-yice lice ong-gel vel heen,
Dah-veeth teerd ad-rev-ah *ch*wahr-a troo-eer glin.
Deh-lin vuh meb-id far-wel ee duh dant,
Dew a*ch* ben-deeth-yo vung weth-oo ahm plant.

ch: pronounced as in "Bach" or the Scotch "loch"
ll: pronounced by very rapidly saying the letters "tl" as if they were one sound, with a strong aspiration.

The Kind Old Man

YR HEN WR MWYN

English lyrics by Llew Tegid

A question-and-answer song, variations of which are frequently found in England and America. The questions should be sung at a slow tempo, and sadly; the old man answers with a jaunty gaiety.

Andante

Where have you been wand-'ring   Kind old man?
Play bee - och chwee neith - your,   ur hen   oor   m'ween? Ur

Kind old man, man, man, man, man, man, man The
hen oor m'ween, m'ween, m'ween, m'ween, m'ween, m'ween, m'ween, Ur

Più mosso

kind - est man a - live. I went out a - fish-in', boys,
hen oor m'ween on - view. Beem un pus - go - ta, boys,

196

Fal dee ree dee ri doh, Fal dee ree dee rid-dle o, Fal dee ree dee ri doh.

Fal dee ree dee ri doh, Fal dee ree dee rid-dle o, Fal dee ree dee ri doh.

poco rit. e dim.

Where have you been wand'ring, kind old man?
  Kind old man, man, man, man, man, man, man,
The kindest man alive.
I went out a-fishin', boys,
  Fal dee ree dee ri doh,
Fal dee ree dee riddle o,
  Fal dee ree dee ri doh.

What have you been getting, kind old man?
  Kind old man, man, man, man, man, man, man,
The kindest man alive.
I caught two fine flatfish, boys,
  Fal dee ree dee ri doh,
Fal dee ree dee riddle o,
  Fal dee ree dee ri doh.

Where had you a wetting, kind old man?
I fell in the river, boys.

What makes you shiver, kind old man?
A cold from the water, boys.

What if you were to die, kind old man?
O, then, you'll bury me, boys.

Where would you be buried, kind old man?
Beneath the old hearthstone, boys.

Why beneath the hearthstone, kind old man?
To hear the porridge bubble, boys.

Play bee-o*ch* *ch*wee neith-your, ur hen oor m'ween?
  Ur hen oor m'ween, m'ween, m'ween, m'ween,
    m'ween, m'ween, m'ween,
Ur hen oor m'ween on-view.
Beem un pus-go-ta, boys,
  Fal dee ree dee ri doh,
Fal dee ree dee riddle o,
  Fal dee ree dee ri doh.

Beth uh thal-ee-a-so*ch*, ur hen oor m'ween?
  Ur hen oor m'ween, m'ween, m'ween, m'ween,
    m'ween, m'ween, m'ween,
Ur hen oor m'ween on-view.
Coo-pool oh led-dod, boys,
  Fal dee ree dee ri doh,
Fal dee ree dee riddle o,
  Fal dee ree dee ri doh.

Play dar-vee *ch*wee oil-uh-*ch*ee, ur hen oor m'ween?
Seerth-ee-oh ee lin uh factory, boys.

Pom eer a*ch* *ch*ween crun-ee, ur hen oor m'ween?
Dim ond tip-in oh on-oid, boys.

Beth pay by'e*ch* un mor-oo, ur hen oor m'ween?
Dim ond vung hlath-ee, boys.

*Ll*ay mun-ne*ch* ei*ch* clahth-ee, ur hen oor m'ween?
Dan gar-eg ur ile-wid, boys.

Beth oon-ei*ch* von hon-o, ur hen oor m'ween?
Goor-an-door yude un froot-yan, boys.

ch: pronounced as in "Bach" or the Scotch "loch"
ll: pronounced by very rapidly saying the letters "tl" as if they were one sound, with a strong aspiration.

197

Men of Harlech

RHYFELGYRCH GWYR HARLECH

Welsh lyrics by Ceriog   *English translation by Peter John Stephens*

Mistakenly called in many reference books "the Welsh National Anthem," this famous march celebrates the defiance of the Welsh forces, under Dafydd ap Jevan, in defending Harlech Castle against the English in 1468. "I held a tower in France till all the old women in Wales heard of it," Dafydd said, "and now all the old women in France shall hear how I defend this castle."

See the glare of fires like hell there, Tongues of flame that writhe and swell there.
Well-uh goil-kairth wen un flam-yo, Ah thav-ode-i tahn un bloyth-yo,

Brave men strike with full-voiced yell there: For-ward with all might.
Ahr eer dew-rion thod ee dah-ro, Een-wythe et on een.

Ar-mor clash-ing, cries of foe-men, Hear the chief-tains ur-ging "on men!"
Gahn-von-llev i tuh-ois-og-yon, Llice gel-on-yon, troost ar-vog-yon

Thun-der of the charg-ing horse-men Ech-o height on height.
Ah char-lom - yod uh march-og - yon, Creig-ar grieg ah green!

Ar-fon sings for-ev-er Of her might and glo-ry.
Ahr-von beeth nee or-veeth, Ken-eer un dra-guh weeth,

Wales will be as Wales has been, So great in free-doms sto-ry. These
Cum-ree veeth vel Cum-ree vee, Un glode-ees um mus-gled-eeth. Ung -

199

See the glare of fires like hell there,
Tongues of flame that writhe and swell there.
Brave men strike with full-voiced yell there:
Forward with all might.
Armor clashing, cries of foemen,
Hear the chieftains urging "On men!"
Thunder of the charging horsemen
Echo height on height.
Arfon sings for ever
Of her might and glory.
Wales will be as Wales has been,
So great in freedom's story.
Those fires light up the sacrifices;
Cry of a dying Welshman rises.
In the cause of freedom's crisis
Bravest men must fight.

Well-uh goil-kairth wen un flam-yo,
Ah thav-ode-i tahn un bloyth-yo,
Ahr eer dew-rion thod ee dah-ro,
Een-wythe et on een.
Gahn von-*llev* i tuh-ois-og-yon,
*Ll*ice gel-on-yon, troost ar-vog-yon,
Ah *ch*ar-lom-yod uh mar*ch*-og-yon,
Creig-ar greig ah green!
Ahr-von beeth nee or-veeth,
Ken-eer un dra-guh weeth,
Cum-ree veeth vel Cum-ree vee,
Un glode-ees um mus gled-eeth.
Ung-ween ohl-i-neer goil-kerth ak-oo,
Tros wev-ees-i Cum-rone mah-roo,
On-nee-bun-yeith seeth un gal-oo,
Am i day-rav deen!

We'll not die, be conquered never.
Harlech, Harlech lives for ever.
Freedom's from the Greatest Giver.
Freedom is our good.
See how Welshmen shouting run down
From the mountains they do come down
Like a storm that strikes at sundown
Boil up like a flood.
Welshmen's strength has made her
Freedom's strong crusader.
Swords of Welshmen have cut deep
The hearts of the invader.
The sword is met by sword replying,
Steel by steel on strength relying;
See where Gwalia's flag is flying,
Freedom's in her blood!

Nee *ch*ife gell-in lath ak-ahm-lid,
Harle*ch*, Harle*ch*, kwed-you hare-lid,
Uh my roth-oor mow'r in ruh-thid,
On-roy mairth ee nee.
Well-uh Gum-ree i buth-in-oy-eth,
Un um-duh-wa*ll*t or mun-uth-oy-eth!
Reeth-rant vel rye-ad-rye duv-roy-eth,
*Ll*amant vel uh *ll*ee!
*Ll*oith-yant een *ll*ee-thee-on!
Roo-ees-tro bar ur es-tron!
Gwi*ch*-bod un i gol-on gife,
Vel brath-uh cleth-ihv Breeth-on;
Uh clairth un air-bin clairth ah *ch*ware-ee,
Deer un air-bin deer ah dare-ee,
Wel-uh von-ner Gwal-ee-i vuh-nee,
Ruh-thid ife ah hee!

ch: pronounced as in "Bach" or the Scotch "loch"
ll: pronounced by very rapidly saying the letters "tl" as if they were one sound, with a strong aspiration.

201

Fairest Gwen

MENTRA GWEN

English translation by Peter John Stephens

This lovely harp tune is the only Welsh song I know of that contains even the slightest hint of improper amatory aggressiveness.

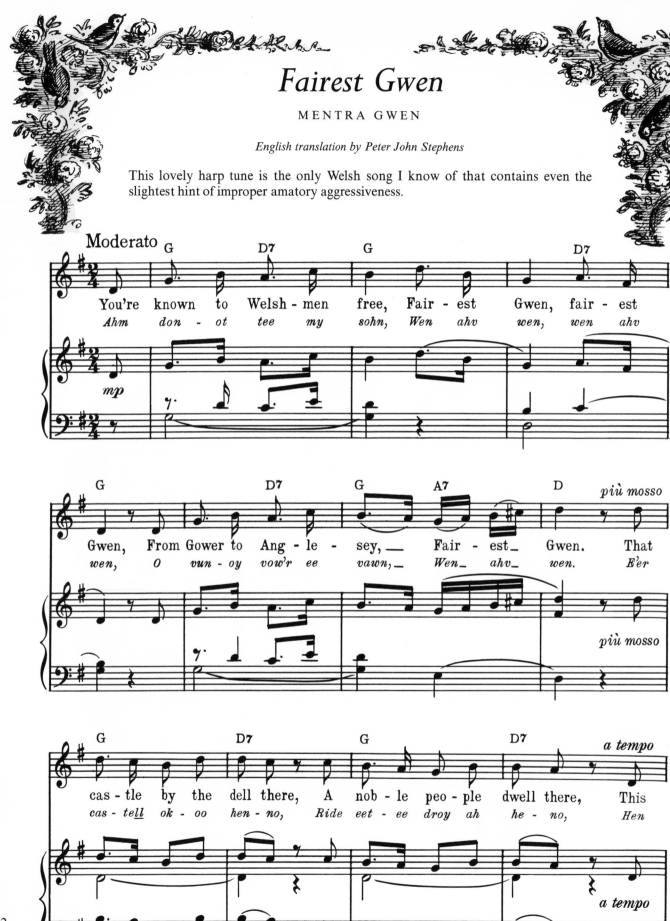

You're known to Welsh-men free, Fair-est Gwen, fair-est
Ahm don - ot tee my sohn, Wen ahv wen, wen ahv

Gwen, From Gower to Ang - le - sey, __ Fair - est __ Gwen. That
wen, O vun - oy vow'r ee vawn, __ Wen __ ahv __ wen. E'er

cas - tle by the dell there, A nob - le peo - ple dwell there, This
cas - tell ok - oo hen - no, Ride eet - ee droy ah he - no, Hen

night we can spend well there, Won't you come now? come now, Gwen.

die - lee own seeth un - tho, Da dee men - tra, men - tra Gwen.

poco rit. e dim.

You're known to Welshmen free,
Fairest Gwen, fairest Gwen,
From Gower to Anglesey,
Fairest Gwen,
That castle by the dell there,
A noble people dwell there.
This night we can spend well there.
Won't you come now? Come now, Gwen.

Do not ride farther on,
Fairest Gwen, fairest Gwen.
The day will soon be gone.
Fairest Gwen,
Oh, put your hand in mine now,
And do not fall behind now.
A castle bed we'll find now.
Won't you come now? Come now, Gwen.

This castle's owned by me,
Fairest Gwen, fairest Gwen.
Inside it you can be,
Fairest Gwen,
As queen of Castle Crogen
For cherished years unbroken,
And take me in the bargain.
Won't you come now? Come now, Gwen.

Ahm don-ot tee my sohn,
Wen ahv wen, wen ahv wen,
O vun-oy vow'r ee von,
Wen ahv wen.
E'er cas-te*ll* ok-oo hen-no,
Ride eet-ee droy ah he-no,
Hen die-lee yown seeth un-tho,
Da dee mentra, mentra Gwen.

Oth fline my mon-eth my'th,
Wen ahv wen, wen ahv wen.
Gwe*ll* ee-tee dor-eeth die'th,
Wen ahv wen.
Wel un vum rike-gahn hun-nee
Uhr ow'n gan ben dare vun-ee,
Vod un uh cas-te*ll* leh-tee,
Da dee mentra, mentra Gwen.

Vee pee-ar cas-te*ll* hoon,
Wen ahv wen, wen ahv wen.
Tee e*ll*-lee view me oon,
Wen ahv wen.
Un rig ung has-te*ll* Cro-gen,
Ee-oo bar*ch*-ee ev i bare-*ch*en,
Ah *ch*um-mur veen uh var-gen,
Da dee mentra, mentra Gwen.

ch: pronounced as in "Bach" or the Scotch "loch"
ll: pronounced by very rapidly saying the letters "tl" as if they were one sound, with a strong aspiration.

Over the Stone

TROS Y GAREG

English lyrics by John Oxenford

A traditional melody. The sentiments expressed are attributed to Rhys Bodychen, who led a contingent of Welsh forces at the Battle of Bosworth Field in 1485.

Moderato

O'er the stone, the grey old stone, Let me pon-der here a-lone,
Trose uh gahr-eg gom-va gee, Et ohn hoy-oo ok un he,

Through all weath-er we to-geth-er Oft have been, thou good old stone.
Vuh an oil-ahv Loy'r-wen lon-ahv, Dov eeth wel-ed un-duh dee.

poco rit.

Of the man-y friends I've seen, Thou the tru-est friend hast been,
Heb een on-ahv, clise nah ch'eev Ahr vuh forth or ruh-vel roo'eev

rit.

Some for-get__ me, some have fled, Some are false, and some are dead,
Cuv - od bah - bell ahr_ uh lon, Gwa - hoth un - o reng uh bon,

Chang-ing nev-er, con-stant ev-er, Still I find_ thee, brave old stone.
Gor - vol - eth - ees Wlad seeth weth - ees Pan thou reese ee un - es von.

poco rit.

O'er the stone, the old gray stone,
Let me ponder here alone,
Through all weather we go together
Ancient stone, thou good old stone.
Of the many friends I've seen,
Thou the truest friend hast been,
Some forget me, some have fled,
Some are false and some are dead,
Changing never, constant ever,
Still I find thee, dear old stone.

Trose uh gahr-eg gom-va gee,
Et ohn hoy-oo ok un he,
Vuh an oil-ahv
Loy'r-wen lon ahv,
Dov eeth wel-ed un duh dee.
Heb een on-ahv, clise nah *ch*'eev
Ahr vuh forth or ruh-vel roo'eev
Cuv-od bah-be*ll* ahr uh lon,
Gwa-hoth un-o reng uh bon,
Gor-vol-eth-ees
Wlad seeth weth-ees
Pan thou reese ee un-es von.

Standing here, thou silent stone,
What a world thou must have known!
Deeds of glory lost to story,
Hast thou witness'd, ancient stone.
Here beneath the grass, 'tis said,
Many warriors bones are laid,
Fighting for their land they fell,
None but thou can truly tell.
Secrets keeping, ever sleeping,
Dream'st thou of the past, old stone?

Cah-voth gor-mess vahr-wol glooee,
Tee-deer you ine bren-nin mooee,
Fol you kise-yo
Nigh tha-vise-yo
Bren-nin ahr-a*ll* maith-eent hooee.
Loy'r-wen lon vuh ile-wid gee,
Ahr vung heith roo-eev vun-hee,
Coo-id duh threig ahr greig-uh-dahn,
Def-ro day-lin Cum-ree lahn:
Gweer uh ken-nin
Meth uh bren-nin
Gahr-yoth eeth-or gor-on hahn!

ch: pronounced as in "Bach" or the Scotch "loch"

ll: pronounced by very rapidly saying the letters "tl" as if they were one sound, with a strong aspiration.

Cuckoo Dear

Y GWCW VACH

English lyrics by Robert Bryan

The melody of this song was first noted by the Reverend Silyn Roberts in Utica, New York (where many Welsh settled upon first coming to America). It was sung to him by a lady who was American born, but who had learned the tune and the first verse of the Welsh lyrics from her Welsh mother. Subsequently, the remainder of the song was recovered from singers in North and Mid-Wales.

Cuckoo dear, why art thou winging,
　Fal de ral de roo, doo ree ri ti toh!
Hither o'er the heather singing,
　Fal de ral de roo, doo ree ri ti toh.
To Dolgelly ere the morrow,
　Fal de ral de roo, de ri ti yoh,
Wend thy way and soothe my sorrow,
　Fal de ral de roo, doo ree ri ti yoh.

Cuckoo dear, my heart's companion,
　Fal de ral de roo, doo ree ri ti toh!
Fly from here across the Wnion,
　Fal de ral de roo, doo ree ri ti toh!
There a moment lightly hover,
　Fal de ral de roo, de ri ti yoh!
O'er the home of my true lover,
　Fal de ral de roo, doo ree ri ti yoh!

Goo-coo va*ch*, ond oit teen fol-og,
　Fal de ral de roo, doo ree ri ti toh!
Can-ee m'leeth eer eith ee'n peeg-og?
　Fal de ral de roo, doo ree ri ti toh.
Dose ee-bloy Doll-g*ell*-ee-deer-yon,
　Fal de ral de roo, de ri ti yoh.
Tee guy un-oh loin-ee gweerth-yon,
　Fal de ral de roo, doo ree ri ti yoh.

Goo-coo va*ch* eh-hed un een-yun,
　Fal de ral de roo, doo ree ri ti toh,
Tee-uh glon eer ahv-un Oon-yun,
　Fal de ral de roo, doo ree ri ti toh;
Ahr duh Ahd-en ahr-ohs en-need,
　Fal de ral de roo, de ri ti yoh,
Oorth un-neth-lay vuh un-oil-id,
　Fal de ral de roo, doo ree ri ti yoh.

208

Cuckoo dear, if there you find him,
    Fal de ral de roo, doo ree ri ti toh!
Sad of cheer, oh perch behind him,
    Fal de ral de roo, doo ree ri ti toh!
Then a Springtide carol sing him,
    Fal de ral de roo, de ri ti yoh!
That shall hope and comfort bring him,
    Fal de ral de roo, doo ree ri ti yoh!

Goo-coo va*ch*, oss un-oh gwail-ee,
    Fal de ral de roo, doo ree ri ti toh,
Ree-oo een iol-ahr dew'r un hail-ee,
    Fal de ral de roo, doo ree ri ti toh;
Can-uh-gon uh gwan-win eeth-o,
    Fal de ral de roo, de ri ti yoh.
Con oh ohb-eith ee-oo gus-eer-o,
    Fal de ral de roo, doo ree ri ti yoh.

ch: pronounced as in "Bach" or the Scotch "loch"
ll: pronounced by very rapidly saying the letters "tl" as if they were one sound, with a strong aspiration.

Megan's Fair Daughter

MERCH MEGAN

English lyrics by John Oxenford

A poignant song telling of what would seem to be an unsatisfactory adjustment to unrequited love.

Andante cantabile

I__ see her in dreams, she trips to me__ light-ly, With__
Me__ well-ice vuh mairch maith Grif-eth ap__ Cun-an, Ahr__

joy on her lips she whis-pers my name. Her__ eyes look in
thew-eth uh leth, pam deeg-yoth vuh meen? Nees__ gwel-ice he

mine so fond-ly so___ bright-ly, I___ wake and 'tis
ree'oid more brud-vairth un___ een-man Kife___ thuv-od un

then no long-er the same. Her glance then is chil-ly, her
ole you hile-wid i heen. Air pam um gad ow-oth mime

poco rit.

step seems to___ shun me, The lips that___ have smil'd wear the___
cahl-on___ ahr___ door-ee; Ong-har-od,___ vung hore-on___ O___

I see her in dreams, she trips to me lightly,
   With joy on her lips she whispers my name.
Her eyes look in mine, so fondly so brightly,
   I wake and 'tis then no longer the same.
Her glance then is chilly, her step seems to shun me,
   The lips that have smiled wear the curl of disdain;
Oh! Megan's fair child my love hath undone me,
   But yet in my dreams I'd see thee again.

Oh, Megan's fair child, in sleep thou art with me,
   Wherever we walk, you go by my side;
Thou hear'st with delight the words I am saying,
   I read thy young heart, I read it with pride.
But ah, when awake if I vow I adore thee,
   Thy look ever tells me I woo thee in vain;
I'll trouble thee not, no more plead before thee;
   I know in my dreams, thou'lt love me again.

Me well-ice vuh mair*ch* maith Grif-eth ap Cun-an,
Ahr thew-eth uh leth, pam deeg-yoth vuh meen?
Nees gwel-ice he ree'oid more brud-vairth un een-man
Kife thuv-od un ole you hile-wid i heen.
Air pam um-gad-ow-oth mine cahl-on ahr door-ee;
Ong-har-od, vung hore-on O math-i ee me.
O nag ay, maith Reece, nid eith-ot mo hon-ee,
Need mair*ch* ee tee oith, Mair*ch* May-gen oith hee.

Mair*ch* May-gen i mam el-ent ad-rev yod-dro
Ok een vee'yu*ch* bob een oo'r o*ll* ahr i *ll*ow;
Ah *ch*er-beed o ower arth-een-ol thou uh-no,
Ee ov-in am bwee, ee Leece An-er-frow.
Un blen-tin mab-ois-yod, pwee god-oid ore ware-in,
Ee Leece uh too-ess-og-yon un hile-wen i vree;
Seen vuh-oid ah goo'res oorth or-seth uh bren-nin?
An reed eth eer tloud, Mair*ch* Mag-gen you hee.

ch: pronounced as in "Bach" or the Scotch "loch"
ll: pronounced by very rapidly saying the letters "tl" as if they were one sound, with a strong aspiration.

212

The Little Saucepan

SOSPAN VACH

English translation by William Cole and Peter John Stephens

Strange to relate, this delightful nonsense is the most famous Rugby football song in Wales. It is particularly identified with the Llanelly team, and it is an awesome thing to hear a huge stadium of Welshmen break out with "Sospan Vach" at a rallying point during a match.

My sweet Mary Ann's hurt her finger, And
My beese Mary Ann wed-dee bree'oo - oh, Ah

David the servant's feeling weak; And the baby's crying now in its
Dahv-ith uh gwas thim un yach. My-ur bah-bahn un uh creed un

cra - dle, The cat's scratching Johnny on the cheek.
cree - oh, Ahr gath wed-dee crahv-ee John-ny bach.

213

Chorus

Sos-pan fach is boil-ing on the fire, Sos-pan fawr boils
Sos-pan vach un bare-we ar uh tahn, Sos-pan vow'r un

ov-er on the floor, The cat's scrath-ing John-ny on the cheek.
bare we ar uh llauer, Ahr gath wed-dee crahv-ee John-ny bach.

Da-vid's a sol-dier, Da-vid's a sol-dier,
Die bach uh soul-joor, Die bach uh soul-joor,

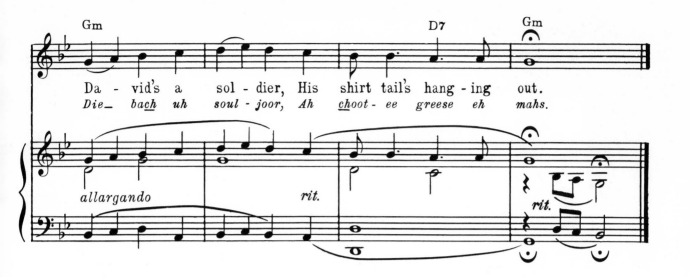

My sweet Mary Ann's hurt her finger,
  And David the servant's feeling weak;
And the baby's crying now in its cradle,
  The cat's scratching Johnny on the cheek
Sospan fach is boiling on the fire,
  Sospan fawr boils over on the floor,
The cat's scratching Johnny on the cheek.
  David's a soldier,
  David's a soldier,
  David's a soldier
  His shirttail's hanging out.

My sweet Mary Ann's feeling better,
  And David the servant's in his grave;
And the baby's sleeping now in his cradle,
  The cat has decided to behave.
Sospan fach is boiling on the fire,
  Sospan fawr boils over on the floor,
The cat has decided to behave.
  David's a soldier,
  David's a soldier,
  David's a soldier,
  With his shirttail hanging out.

My beese Mary Ann wed-dee bree'oo-oh,
Ah Dahv-ith uh gwas thim un ya*ch*.
My-ur bah-bahn un uh creed un cree-oh,
Ahr gath wed-dee crahv-ee John-ny ba*ch*.
Sos-pan va*ch* un bare-we ar uh tahn,
Sos-pan vow'r un bare we ar uh *ll*auer,
Ahr gath wed-dee crahv-ee John-ny ba*ch*.
Die ba*ch* uh soul-joor,
Die ba*ch* uh soul-joor,
Die ba*ch* uh soul-joor
Ah *ch*oot-ee greese eh mahs.

My beese Mary Ann wed-dee goo-eh-*ll*uh,
Ah Dahv-ith uh gwas un i vaith.
My-ur bah-bahn un uh creed wed-dee teh-wee,
Ahr gath wed-ee hee-no meh-oon haith.
Sos-pan va*ch* un bare-we ar uh tahn,
Sos-pan vow'r un bare we ar uh *ll*auer,
Ahr gath we-dee hee-no me-own haith.
Die ba*ch* uh soul-joor,
Die ba*ch* uh soul-joor,
Die ba*ch* uh soul-joor
Ah *ch*oot-ee greese eh mahs.

Sospan fach: (pronounced "vach" as in "Bach") little saucepan. *Sospan fawr:* (pronounced "vow'r") big saucepan.

ch: pronounced as in "Bach" or the Scotch "loch"

ll: pronounced by very rapidly saying the letters "tl" as if they were one sound, with a strong aspiration.

The Ash Grove

LLWYN ON

One of the few Welsh folk songs that has become part of the folk-song heritage all over the world. According to *Grove's Dictionary of Music and Musicians,* it appeared "in a mutilated form as 'Cease Your Funning' in John Gay's *The Beggar's Opera* in 1728."

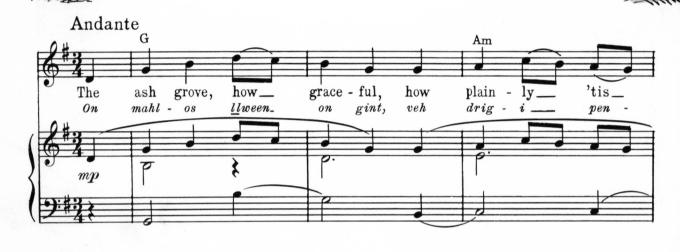

The ash grove, how＿ grace-ful, how plain-ly 'tis＿ speak-ing,
On mahl - os llween＿ on gint, veh drig - i＿ pen - dev - ig,

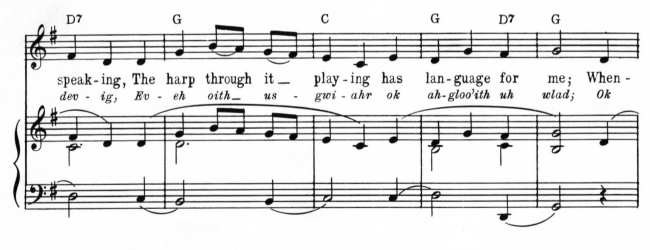

The harp through it＿ play-ing has lan-guage for me; When-
Ev - eh oith＿ us - gwi - ahr ok ah-gloo'ith uh wlad; Ok

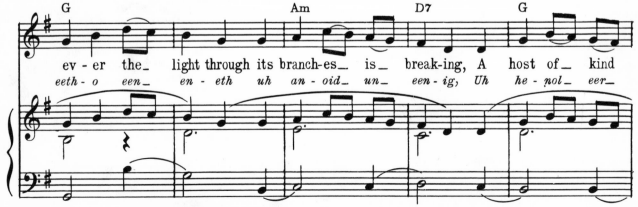

ev - er the＿ light through its branch-es＿ is＿ break-ing, A host of＿ kind
eeth - o een＿ en - eth uh an - oid＿ un＿ een - ig, Uh he - nol＿ eer＿

216

217

The ash grove, how graceful, how plainly 'tis speaking,
The harp through it playing has language for me;
Whenever the light through its branches is breaking,
A host of kind faces is gazing on me.
The friends of my childhood again are before me,
Each step wakes a mem'ry, as freely I roam;
With soft whispers laden, its leaves rustle o'er me;
The ash grove, the ash grove alone is my home.

My lips smile no more, my heart loses its lightness,
No dream of the future my spirit can cheer;
I only can brood on the past and its brightness,
The dead I have mourned are again living here.
From ev'ry dark nook they press forward to meet me;
I lift up my eyes to the broad leafy dome,
And others are there, looking downward to greet me;
The ash grove, the ash grove alone is my home.

On mahl-os *ll*ween on gint, veh drig-i pen-dev-ig,
Ev-eh oith us-gwi-ahr ok ah-gloo'ith uh wlad;
Ok eeth-o een en-eth uh an-oid un een-ig,
Uh he-nol eer hon-es oith ire-es i thod.
Eith car-yod you gwail-ed, un lan uh feer lenk-en,
Ond cod-ire us gwi-ahr un ov-ahr ok air*ch*,
Ee saith-eer ba*ch* gen-en, ond gweer-oth i lin-in,
I air-ged un oor-gam ee vun-wes i vair*ch*.

Rhee hweer ud-oith gol-oo uh saith ot uh *ll*in-in,
Ahr *ll*an-kess un mor-oo un well-oo ah gwan;
Bug-uth-yoith i gleth-uv troo-ee gol-on uh *ll*en-kin,
Ond nee red-i car-yod een vod-veth or von.
Royth gol-id i dar-par un hen ok on-een-od,
Uh gur-yi dew eth-av eer ire-ess harth hon,
Oith gwe*ll* gen-eev var-oo troo-ee air-ged vung har-yod,
Nah bew gid-da go-leed un muh-ha-lahs *ll*ween on.

ch: pronounced as in "Bach" or the Scotch "loch"
ll: pronounced by very rapidly saying the letters "tl" as if they were one sound, with a strong aspiration.

218

Rise, Rise, Thou Merry Lark

CODIAD YR HEDYDD

One of the many pastoral folk tunes celebrating the beauties of nature.

Moderato

Rise, rise thou mer-ry lark, Whose up-ward flight I love to mark At
Clee'oo, clee'oo, vor - i - ol glod, O! vwee-ned yoor dev - nen-ine dod, O

ear-ly dawn of day. Leave, leave thy mos-sy lair, With light wing cleave the
oon - va lan ee lowr. I mon thev-nin nigh con, On i - riv lee, ree'you

yield-ing air And car-ol forth thy lay! Sweet, oh sweet the hon-ied note That
deer - va lon, Thee - hon-goth geed ahr wow'r? Meed your ow - el ahr uh wow'n, Uh

219

swells with-in thy warb-ling throat! 'Tis a stream of mel - o - dy That stems the rap-tured
breeg uh greeg un es-mwith green; Goo'ron-do my - eer ob - er gein, Ok un uh broon em-

soul a - way, De - light-ful har - bin - ger of day My bless-ing go with thee!
geeth-ya heen; More neh - vol sairch-ol ud yoor sine, Seen dod ee sween-o deen.

220

Rise, rise, thou merry lark,
Whose upward flight I love to mark
    At early dawn of day.
Leave, leave thy mossy lair,
With light wing cleave the yielding air
    And carol forth thy lay!
Sweet, oh sweet the honied note
That swells within thy warbling throat!
    'Tis a stream of melody
That steals the raptured soul away,
Delightful harbinger of day
    My blessing go with thee!

Night's ling'ring shades are fled,
And Phoebus, from his ocean bed
    Through aether wings his flight.
Oh! let thy music sweet
His presence with glad welcome greet
    In ditties of delight!
Higher yet, still higher fly
Still soaring upward to the sky;
    As when, in Eden's fairest grove
Unto the new created pair
You first did tune, to music rare,
    A merry song of love!

Clee'oo, clee'oo, vor-i-ol glod,
O! vwee-ned your dev-nen-ine dod,
O oon-va lan ee lowr.
I mon thev-nin nigh con,
On i-riv lee, ree'you deer-va lon,
Thee-hon-goth geed ahr wow'r?
Meed your ow-el ahr uh wow'n,
Uh breeg uh greeg un es-mwith green;
Goo'ron-do my-eer ob-er gein,
Ok un uh broon em-geeth-ya heen;
More neh-vol sair*ch* -ol ud yoor sine,
Seen dod ee sween-o deen.

Kweed, kweed, eh hed-ith, kweed,
O lay ee lay ar od-en l'wid,
Un ee'oo*ch,* un ee'oo*ch* o heed;
Can, can, duh nod i kee,
Ah dos un nes ot lah-wen lee,
Ad ow-woth boin uh beed.
Con-ee my, ahr beed uh glee'oo
I ol-ow lon O ee*ch*-el lay,
Cuf-id heer-i-eth don-nol ree'oo,
Ahr ol i lice ee vroy-eth nay;
Un nes at theeth un nes at thee'oo,
Ee von-nee vel ev-vay!

ch: pronounced as in "Bach" or the Scotch "loch"
ll: pronounced by very rapidly saying the letters "tl" as if they were one sound, with a strong aspiration.

Lullaby

SUO GAN

One of the purest and loveliest lullabies in the world of folk song. It first began to turn up in song collections in 1800, and this version, now the standard one, was collected by the folk-song scholar Robert Bryan.

Andante

Sleep, my ba - by, on my bos - om, Warm and cos - y will it prove;
Heen uh blen - tin ar vuh mon - wes, Cleed uh chun - nes ahd - you hon;

Round thee moth-er's arms are fold-ing, In her heart a moth-er's love.
Brych - yi mom seen deen om don - ot, Car - yod mom see don vum ron;

There shall no one come to harm thee, Naught shall ev - er break thy rest;
Nee cha dim ahm har - eeth gon - teen, Newn - na een - deen ah thee gahm;

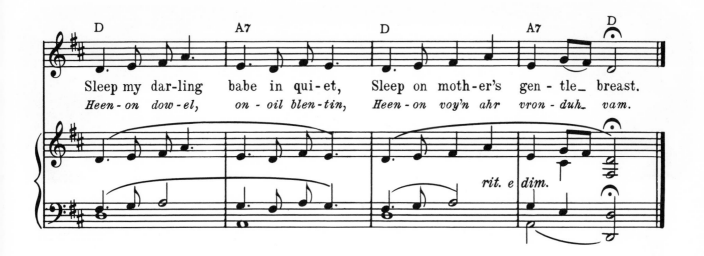

Sleep my dar-ling babe in qui-et, Sleep on moth-er's gen-tle breast.
Heen-on dow-el, on-oil blen-tin, Heen-on voy'n ahr vron-duh vam.

rit. e dim.

Sleep, my baby, on my bosom,
   Warm and cozy will it prove;
Round thee mother's arms are folding,
   In her heart a mother's love.
There shall no one come to harm thee,
   Naught shall ever break thy rest;
Sleep, my darling babe, in quiet,
   Sleep on mother's gentle breast.

Sleep serenely, baby, slumber,
   Lovely baby, gently sleep;
Tell me wherefore art thou smiling,
   Smiling sweetly in thy sleep?
Do the angels smile in heaven
   When thy happy smile they see?
Dost thou on them smile while slum'bring
   On my bosom peacefully.

Heen-uh blen-tin ar vuh mon-wes,
Cleed uh *ch*un-nes ahd-you hon;
Bry*ch*-yi mom seen deen om don-ot,
Car-yod mom see don vum ron;
Nee *ch*a dim ahm har-eeth gon-teen,
Newn na een-deen ah thee gahm;
Heen-on dow-el, on-oil blen-tin,
Heen-on voy'n ahr vron duh vam.

Heen-on dow-el, hen-o, heen-uh,
Heen-on voy-en, uh t'loose i leen;
Pam-ur oit un ower-un gwen-ee,
Gwen-een deer-yon un duh heen?
I ang-gull-yon vree seen gwen-ee,
Ahr not tee un gwen-een-*ll*on?
Tee-thine gwen-een ole done heen-o,
Heen-awn dow-el ahr vum-ron?

Pide og ov-nee, dim on dile-en,
Geer-uh, geer-uh ahr uh thor;
Pide og ov-nee, ton va*ch* een-ig,
See-ah see-ahr lan uh more.
Heen-uh blen-tin, need ois um-mah,
Thim ee rah-thee ee-tee-vrah-ow;
Gwen-an dow-el un vuh mon-wes,
Ahr ur eng-gul gwin-yon drah-oo.

ch: pronounced as in "Bach" or the Scotch "loch"
ll: pronounced by very rapidly saying the letters "tl" as if they were one sound, with a strong aspiration.

All through the Night

AR HYD Y NOS

The best-known Welsh folk song, this has become a standard on the concert stage, and with choirs, for the past century.

Andante cantabile

Sleep, my love, and peace at-tend thee, All through the night;
Holl am ran-tire sehr thuh wed-ont, Ahr heed uh nohs.

Guard-ian an-gels God will lend thee, All through the night.
Dum-ar forth ee vro go-gawn-yont, Ahr heed uh nohs.

Soft the drow-sy hours are creep-ing, Hill and vale in slum-ber steep-ing,
Gol-i ar-all you tuh wull ooch, Ee are thang os gweer bred vairtch-ooch,

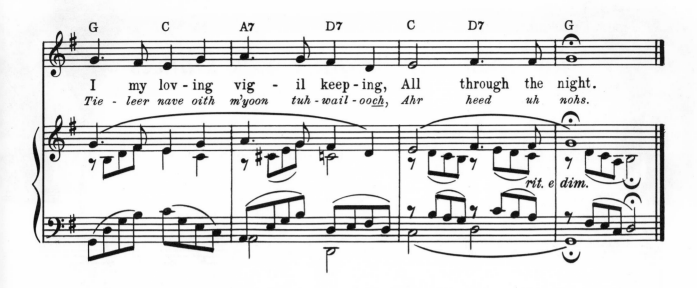

I my lov-ing vig-il keep-ing, All through the night.
Tie - leer nave oith m'yoon tuh-wail-ooch, Ahr heed uh nohs.

rit. e dim.

Sleep, my love, and peace attend thee,
    All through the night;
Guardian angels God will lend thee,
    All through the night.
Soft the drowsy hours are creeping,
Hill and vale in slumber steeping,
I my loving vigil keeping,
    All through the night.

Angels watching ever round thee,
    All through the night;
In thy slumbers close surround thee,
    All through the night.
They should of all fears disarm thee,
No forebodings should alarm thee,
They will let no peril harm thee,
    All through the night.

Ho*ll* am ran-tire sehr thuh wed-ont,
Ahr heed uh nohs.
Dum-ar forth ee vro go-gawn-yont,
Ahr heed uh nohs.
Gol-i ar-a*ll* you tuh wu*ll*-oo*ch*,
Ee are thang os gweer bred vair*tch*-oo*ch*,
Tie-leer nave oith m'yoon tuh-wail-oo*ch*,
Ahr heed uh nohs.

Oh more seer-yol gwen ah sare-en,
Ahr heed uh nohs.
Ee o-ly-yo'ee *ch*wire thy-are-en,
Ahr heed uh nohs.
Nohs you hen-eint pan thou cus-teeth,
Ond ee har-thee deen i hoorth-theeth,
Rone ein goal-i gwan een gil-eeth,
Ahr heed uh nohs.

ch: pronounced as in "Bach" or the Scotch "loch"
ll: pronounced by very rapidly saying the letters "tl" as if they were one sound, with a strong aspiration.

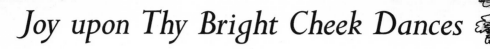

Joy upon Thy Bright Cheek Dances

HOB Y DERI DANDO

This delicate song is distantly related to "Hai Down ir Deri Danno," an old song of the Druids. The meaning of "Hob Y Deri Dando" in Welsh is "the pig under the oaks." There are two versions of this song popular in Wales; this is the North Wales version.

Moderato

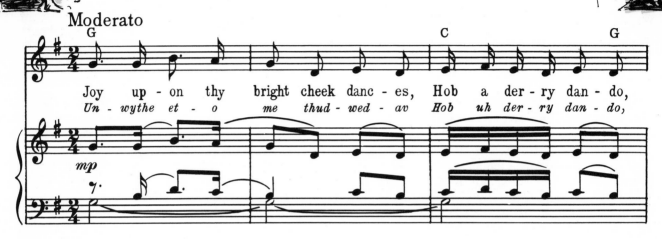

Joy up-on thy bright cheek danc-es, Hob a der-ry dan-do,
Un - wythe et - o me thud-wed-av Hob uh der-ry dan-do,

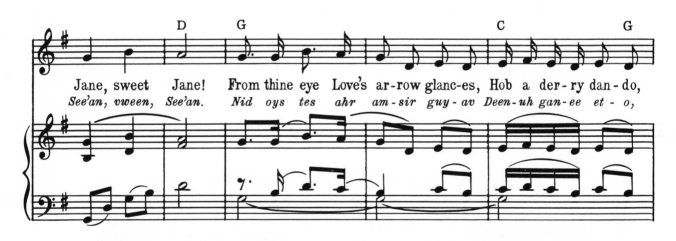

Jane, sweet Jane! From thine eye Love's ar-row glanc-es, Hob a der-ry dan-do,
See'an, vween, See'an. Nid oys tes ahr am-sir guy-av Deen-uh gan-ee et-o,

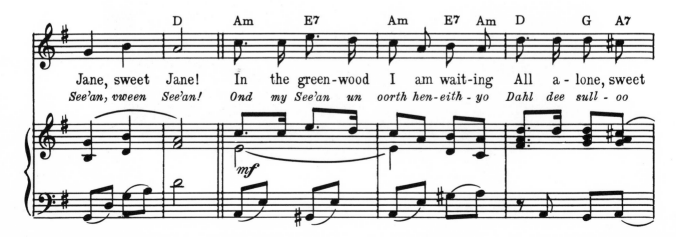

Jane, sweet Jane! In the green-wood I am wait-ing All a-lone, sweet
See'an, vween See'an! Ond my See'an un oorth hen-eith-yo Dahl dee sull-oo

226

Jane; To the tune-ful birds re-lat-ing How I love thee, Jane;
See'an! Ev - o cahr-yod un gwev-writhe-yo See'an voo'en, teer'd eer *lloin*,

Come un-to the tryst-ing tree, Jane, sweet Jane!
Sine - yav en - oo See'on - ee vween, See'an, vween, See'an.

mp rit. e dim.

Joy upon thy bright cheek dances,
    Hob a derry dando, Jane, sweet Jane!
From thine eye Love's arrow glances,
    Hob a derry dando, Jane, sweet Jane!
In the greenwood I am waiting
    All alone, sweet Jane;
To the tuneful birds relating
    How I love thee, Jane;
Come unto the trysting tree,
    Jane, sweet Jane!

Oh! that wingèd were thy lover,
    Hob a derry dando, Jane, sweet Jane!
Round thee like a dove to hover,
    Hob a derry dando, Jane, sweet Jane!
Think not I can ever leave thee,
    No! such thought is vain!
Think not I could e'er deceive thee;
    Oh, no! pretty Jane!
Thou art all the world to me,
    Jane, sweet Jane!

Un-wythe et-o me thuh-wed-av
Hob uh derry dan-do, See'an, vween, See'an.
Nid oys tes ahr am-sir guy-av
Deen-uh gan-ee et o, See'an, vween, See'an!
Ond my See'an un oorth hen-eith-yo
Dahl dee sull-oo See'an!
Ev-o cahr-yod un gwev-writhe-yo
See'an voo'en, teer'd eer *ll*oin,
Sine-yav en-oo See'on-ee vween,
See'an, vween, See'an.

*Ll*ower guy-ov hav uh gwan-win
Hob uh derry dan-do, See'an, vween, See'an?
Oo-neith veen voil uh theeth-ine vel-in:
Deen-uh gan-ee et-o, See'an, vween, See'an.
Need you hen-eint o een d'yon-ee;
Dahl see sull-oo See'an,
Ee naid cahr-yod yay-ank oyer-ree:
See'an, vween, teer'd eer *ll*oin,
Sine-yav en-oo See'on'ee vween,
See'an, vween, See'an.

ch: pronounced as in "Bach" or the Scotch "loch"
ll: pronounced by very rapidly saying the letters "tl" as if they were one sound, with a strong aspiration.

Idle Days in Summertime

BUGEILIO'R GWENITH GWYN

English lyrics by Walter Maynard

This is the best known of the many songs written by William Hopcyn, known as "Will Hopcyn, The Bard," who was born in 1700. Tradition has it that the song is based on an unconsummated love between The Bard and Ann Thomas. The story of the love is told in a novel, *The Maid of Cefn Ydfa*, once popular throughout Wales.

I - dle days in sum-mer time, In pleas-ant sun - ny weath-er, A-
Me seeth vach-gen ye-yank foll, Un b'you un ol vuh fon-cee Muh

mid the gold-en col-ored corn, Two lov-ers passed to-geth-er.
veen be - gile-yor gwen-eth gwin, Ok ar-all un i ved-dee.

There were words they did not speak To give their thoughts ex-press-ion; Each
Pam nath-oy-ee ahr vuh ole, Ree'oo theeth ar ole i geel-eth? Gwyth

228

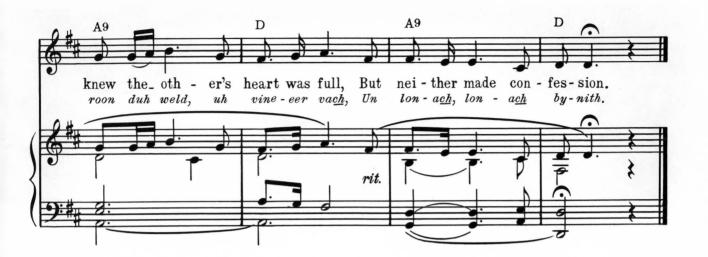

knew the_ oth - er's heart was full, But nei - ther made con - fes - sion.
roon duh weld, uh vine-eer vach, Un lon-ach, lon - ach by-nith.

Idle days in summertime,
   In pleasant sunny weather,
Amid the golden colored corn,
   Two lovers passed together.
There were words they did not speak
   To give their thoughts expression;
Each knew the other's heart was full,
   But neither made confession.

Winter came, and then, alas!
   Came cold and dreary weather;
No more the lovers passed their days
   Amid the fields together.
Fate had severed them apart,
   And now they're brokenhearted;
Had they been wed in summertime,
   They would not now be parted.

Me seeth vach-gen yi-yonk fole,
Uu b'you un ol vuh fon-cee
Muh veen be-gile-yor gwen-eth gwin,
Ok ar-all un i ved-dee.
Pam nath-oy-ee ahr vuh ole,
Ree'oo theeth ar ole i geel-eth?
Gwyth roon duh weld, uh vine-eer vach,
Un lon-ach, lon-ach by-nith.

Glon-ach, lon-ach oit bob deeth,
Nigh vee see'an feeth un fole-ach,
Air moin uh goorah-oo-nyeth duh weth,
Goo-nah eem dreeg-ar-eth bell-ach.
Coon duh ben, gwel ok-oo drow,
Rho ee meeth lah-oo wen deer-yon;
Gwyth un duh vun-wes bairt i throw
My all-weth clo vung hal-lon!

Cod-ice heth-you gud-ahr wow'r,
Gan vrees-yon vowr vuh lleeth-ed;
Vel kown geese-on-ee ol duh droyd
Ahr heed uh kwed oorth gairth-ed.
Coon-nah hane ohr gol-ahr mythe,
Ah sairch-ees yeith goor-een-eb;
Gwithe moo-ee nahr beed eer mob ath gahr,
You gol-oog ahr duh ween-eb.

Tra bo dew'r uh more un hallt,
Uh thra bung wallt un tuh-vee
Uh thra bo col-on dan-vum ron
Me veeth-ahn futh-lon ee-tee;
Dow-ed eem-eer gweer don gel
Ah row don sell dat-eb-yon,
Peen i muh-vee nigh ar-all, On,
Seeth ohr-i gon duh gol-lon.

ch: pronounced as in "Bach" or the Scotch "loch"
ll: pronounced by very rapidly saying the letters "tl" as if they were one sound, with a strong aspiration.

Counting the Goats
CYFRI'R GIEFR

English translation by William Cole and Peter John Stephens

There are many versions of this tongue twister found in rural Wales. It is an example of the singing games with which the farmhands would amuse one another during the long winter nights around the fire. The trick is to sing the repeat of the chorus as fast as can be managed and still maintain distinct enunciation.

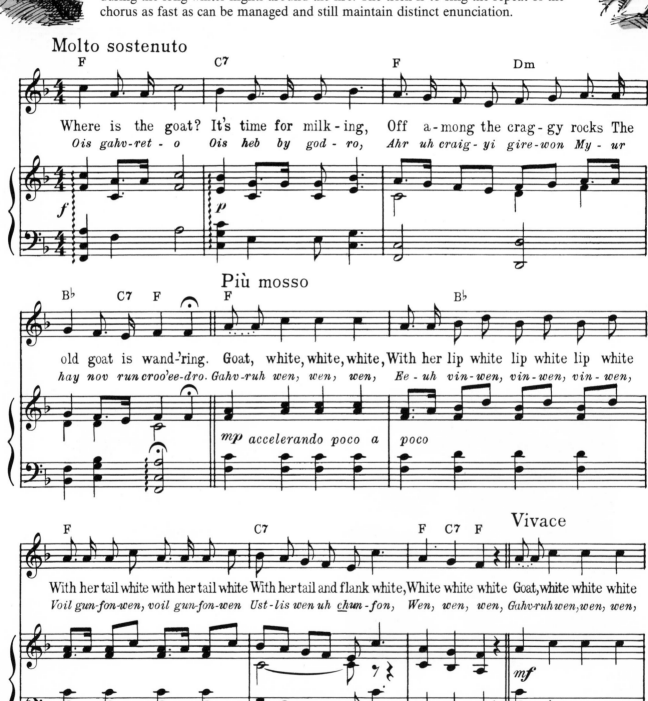

Molto sostenuto

Where is the goat? It's time for milk-ing, Off a-mong the crag-gy rocks The
Ois gahv-ret - o   Ois heb by god - ro,   Ahr uh craig - yi gire-won My - ur

Più mosso

old goat is wand-'ring. Goat, white, white, white, With her lip white lip white lip white
hay nov run croo'ee-dro. Gahv-ruh wen, wen, wen,   Ee - uh vin-wen, vin-wen, vin-wen,

mp accelerando poco a poco

Vivace

With her tail white with her tail white With her tail and flank white, White white white Goat, white white white
Voil gun-fon-wen, voil gun-fon-wen Ust-lis wen uh chun-fon, Wen, wen, wen, Gahv-ruh wen, wen, wen,

mf

With her lip white lip white lip white With her tail white with her tail white With her tail and flank white White white white.

Ee-uh vin-wen, vin-wen, vin-wen, Voil gun fon-wen, voil gun-fon-wen Ust-lis wen uh chun-fon Wen, wen, wen.

Where is the goat?
It's time for milking,
Off among the craggy rocks
The old goat is wand'ring.

Goat white, white, white,
With her lip white, lip white, lip white,
With her tail white, with her tail white,
With her tail and flank white,
White, white, white.

Goat white, white, white,
With her lip white, lip white, lip white,
With her tail white, with her tail white,
With her tail and flank white,
White, white, white.

Ois gahv-ret-o,
Ois heb by god-ro,
Ahr uh craig-yi gire-won
My'ur hay nov run croo'ee-dro.

*Gahv-ruh wen, wen, wen,
Ee-uh vin-wen, vin-wen, vin-wen,
Voil gun-fon-wen, voil gun-fon-wen,
Ust-lis wen uh chun-fon,
Wen, Wen, wen.*

*Gahv-ruh wen, wen, wen,
Ee-uh vin-wen, vin-wen, vin-wen,
Voil gun-fon-wen, voil gun-fon-wen,
Ust-lis wen uh chun-fon,
Wen, Wen, wen.*

Note: The succeeding verses have the same lyrics save for changing the color referred to each time. The second verse should be "black" "thee," the third "red" ("go*ch*"), the fourth "blue" ("lahs"). Thus:

*Goat black, black, black,
With her lip black, lip black, lip black, etc.*

*Gahv-ruh thee, thee, thee,
Ee-uh vin-thee, vin-thee, vin-thee, etc.*

ch: pronounced as in "Bach" or the Scotch "loch"
ll: pronounced by very rapidly saying the letters "tl" as if they were one sound, with a strong aspiration.

The Dove

Y DERYN PUR

A beautiful traditional song which first turned up in print in a famous group of national airs gathered by the folk-song collector Jane Williams. She was awarded first prize "for the best collection of unpublished Welsh music" at the Abergavenny Eisteddfod (musical and literary festival) in 1837.

Moderato

One day as I in mer-ry mood, O'er mead-ow green was stray-ing, I
Uh dare-in peer ahr ah-dine-lahs Beeth eem-een whas_ dee brud-dur. O

spied a maid-en pass-ing fair A - mid the lamb-kins play-ing;
bros-eer bros-ya ot-uh vairch, Llay roice eem sairch un gun nar;

None so pret-ty, none so wit-ty, E'er was seen in town or cit-y;
Dose tee ot-tee, duh-wed orth-ee, Mode een oil-or dewr un hale-ee;

232

Sweet-ly smil-ing, and be-guil-ing, She stole my heart a - way for-ev-er; O
*Mode een eer - ad, om i gwale-ed, Ok oy — char-yod— un file-yah char*e-thed O

maid - en fair be - yond com-pare, For - get thee can I nev - er.
dew vuth - i - or hearth i lleen Om boy - nee deen— more gal - led.

One day as I in merry mood,
  O'er meadow green was straying,
I spied a maiden passing fair
  Amid the lambkins playing;
None so pretty, none so witty,
  E'er was seen in town or city;
Sweetly smiling, and beguiling,
  She stole my heart away forever;
O maiden fair beyond compare,
  Forget thee can I never.

Come, gentle dove, with azure wing,
  And listen to my ditty;
Go seek the maid and try to move
  Her bosom unto pity;
When you meet her, kindly greet her,
  And with lovely notes entreat her;
Softly cooing, sweetly wooing,
  O, say my heart is hers forever!
O maiden fair beyond compare,
  Forget thee can I never!

Uh dare-in peer ahr ah-dine-lahs
Beeth eem-een whas dee brud-dur.
O bros-eer bros-ya ot-uh vair*ch;*
*Ll*ay roice eem sair*ch* un gun-nar;
Dose tee ot-tee, duh-wed oorth-ee,
Mode een oil-or dewr un hale-ee;
Mode een eer-add, om i gwale-ed,
Ok oy *ch*ar-yod un file-yah *ch*are-thed
O dew vuth-i-or harth i *ll*een
Om boy-nee deen more gal-led.

Pon ow'en un hoy-niece yown vuh hoil.
Thew-ar-nod goil un gwil-yo,
Can-vuth-oon ven-you lan-ar ree-oid,
Ahr us-gown droy'd un rod-yo.
Pon i gwale-ice seeth me say-vice,
Un vung hol-lon me veth-uh lee-ice
Well-lay thee-ness lon-ahr dire-nas,
I gwen un harth-eer o*ll* oy *ch*oom-pahs,
Nee vun-soon gred-dee een deen b'yew,
Nad oith hee ree-you on-gul-les.

ch: pronounced as in "Bach" or the Scotch "loch"
ll: pronounced by very rapidly saying the letters "tl" as if they were one sound, with a strong aspiration.

Welsh National Anthem

HEN WLAD FY NHADAU

Welsh lyrics by Evan James
English translation by Peter John Stephens

Music by James James

One of the very few really fine and moving national anthems, this is sung by Welshmen en masse on every possible occasion.

Moderato maestoso

Oh land of my fa-ther's, oh dear land to_ me, The
My hen lad vun had-i un on-oil ee_ me, Gwlad

land of the po-ets and sing-ers is she. Her_ he-roes of_
by'urth uh chon-tor-yon, en wog-yon o vree; I_ goor-ul ruh-

his-t'ry so_ brave-ly they_ stood And fought for their coun-try and good._
vel-weer, gwlad-gar-weer tra_ mod, Trose ruh-thed goll as-ont i gwide._

234

Chorus

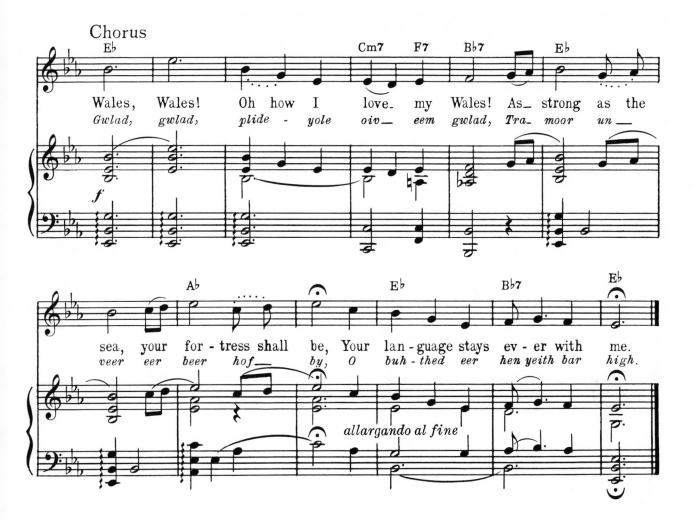

Wales, Wales! Oh how I love my Wales! As strong as the
Gwlad, gwlad, plide - yole oiv— eem gwlad, Tra moor un —

sea, your for - tress shall be, Your lan - guage stays ev - er with me.
veer eer beer hof— by, O buh - thed eer hen yeith bar high.

allargando al fine

Oh land of my fathers, oh dear land to me,
The land of the poets and singers is she.
Her heroes of hist'ry so bravely they stood
And fought for their country and good.

Wales, Wales! Oh how I love my Wales!
As strong as the sea, your fortress shall be,
Your language stays ever with me.

A haven of poets lies under Welsh skies,
Each valley and hill is the pride of my eyes.
The love of my land and the song of her streams
Forever remains in my dreams.
Chorus:

Though foreign oppression may lie on my land,
The language of Wales shall forever withstand.
The muse will not die though my country's betrayed,
The songs of her bright harp not fade.
Chorus:

My hen lad vun had-i un on-oil ee me,
Gwlad by'urth uh *ch*on-tor-yon, en wog-yon o vree;
I goor-ul ruh-vel-weer, gwlad-gar-weer tra mod,
Trose ruh-thed go*ll* as-ont i gwide.

Gwlad, gwlad, plide-yole oiv eem gwlad,
Tra moor un veer eer beer hof by,
O buh-thed eer hen-yeith bar high.

Hen Gum-ree vun-ith-ig, par-od-wees uh barth,
Pob duf-rin, pob clog-win, eem gol-oog seeth harth;
Troy dime-lad gwlad-gahr-ol more sween-nol you see,
I nen-teeth, av-on-ith ee me.
Chorus:

Os trice-yoth uh gel-lin vung lad don i droy'd,
My hen-yeith uh Cum-ree more view ag air-yoid;
Nee leeth-ee-wid ur ow-wen gon air*ch*-u*ll* lah'oo brod,
Nah they-lin beer-sine-yol vung wlad.
Chorus:

ch: pronounced as in "Bach" or the Scotch "loch"
ll: pronounced by very rapidly saying the letters "tl" as if they were one sound, with a strong aspiration.

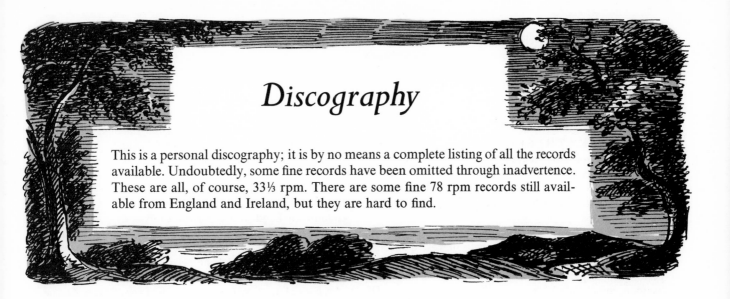

Discography

This is a personal discography; it is by no means a complete listing of all the records available. Undoubtedly, some fine records have been omitted through inadvertence. These are all, of course, 33⅓ rpm. There are some fine 78 rpm records still available from England and Ireland, but they are hard to find.

BARRY, MARGARET, *Songs of an Irish Tinker Lady,* Riverside RLP 12-602 12″. An authentic gypsy street singer performs in a style that is surprising at first, but is well worth getting used to. Includes "She Moved Through the Fair," "My Lagan Love," and "The Bold Fenian Men."

BRAND, OSCAR, *Bawdy Songs and Backroom Ballads, Vol. I,* Audio Fidelity AFLP 1906 12″. Spirited renditions of English and American earthy songs. I especially favor "One-Eyed Reilly" and "Blow the Candle Out."

CAMERON, ISLA, *Through Bushes and Briers* and other songs of the British Isles, Tradition TLP1001 12″. An exciting voice and moving artistry. Every song on the record is noteworthy; I would signal out "Keel Row," "To the Begging I Will Go," "The Water Is Wide," "Died for Love," "Baloo Baleary," and "The Cherry Tree Carol."

CLANCY BROTHERS (Tom, Liam, and Patrick) AND TOMMY MAKEM, *Come Fill Your Glass with Us,* Tradition TLP 1032 12″. A total delight; especially fine are "Finnigan's Wake," (Liam Clancy) "A Jug of Punch," (Patrick Clancy), and the finest performance I've ever heard of "The Parting Glass" (Liam Clancy).

CLANCY BROTHERS (Tom, Liam, and Patrick) AND TOMMY MAKEM, *The Rising of the Moon,* Irish songs of rebellion, Tradition TLP 1006 12″. Rousing renditions of such songs as "The Rising of the Moon," "O'Donnell Aboo," and "The Minstrel Boy." Liam Clancy's delicate rendering (of the English) in "Whack Fol the Diddle" is praiseworthy.

CLAYTON, PAUL, *Bobby Burns' Merry Muses of Caledonia,* Elektra 155 12″. The most unblushingly earthy songs ever written, sung without a leer. Especially recommended: "John Anderson, My Jo" and "Tommie Makes My Tail Toddle."

CLAYTON, PAUL, *British Broadside Ballads in Popular Tradition,* Folkways FW 8708 12″. Exciting songs sung with purity and musical intelligence, especially "Pleasant and Delightful," "Three Maidens to Milking Did Go," "When Pat Came over the Hill," and "The Dark-Eyed Sailor."

COPPARD, AUDREY, *English Folk Songs,* Folkways FP 917 10″. Miss Coppard sings purely and beautifully. I particularly like her "Hares on the Mountain" (sung from the feminine point of view), "I Will Give My Love an Apple," and "The Trees Are Getting High."

DELLER, ALFRED, *The Three Ravens,* English folk songs, Vanguard VRS 479 12″. The highest voice in Christendom singing beautiful old songs. Notable are "The Cuckoo," "The Oak and the Ash," "Coventry Carol," and "Greensleeves."

DUNBAR, MAX, *Songs and Ballads of the Scottish Wars,* Folkways FP 3006 12″. Spirited and straightforward rendition of such fine songs as "The Piper O'Dundee," "Will Ye Go to Sheriffmuir?," "Johnnie Cope," and "Awa', Whigs, Awa'."

DYER-BENNETT, RICHARD, *Songs:* a series of nine 12″ records, sold under the singer's own label. One of the great performers of our time, there is no one who sings so beautifully "A May Day Carol" and "The Three Ra'ens" (record 4), and "Oft in the Stilly Night" (record 1). Record 2 has fine performances of "Cock Robin," "Blow the Candles Out," and "Two Maids Went Milking."

ENGLAND, The Columbia World Library of Folk and Primitive Music, edited by Peter Kennedy and Alan Lomax, Columbia KL-206 12″. A must for every folk song collection; authentic taped instrumental and vocal performances, including some songs by the great folk singer Phil Tanner.

EVANS, MERÉDYDD, *Welsh Folk Songs,* Folkways FP 835 10″. A young Welshman, now living in America, sings, unaccompanied, with great purity and musical taste. Notable are "Cyfri'r Geifr" ("Counting the Goats"), "Robin Ddiog" ("Lazy Robin"), "Bugeilio'r Gwenith Gwyn" ("Idle Days in Summer Time" in this book), and "Yr Hen Wr Mwyn" ("The Kind Old Man")

FERRIER, KATHLEEN, *Folk Songs, Northumbrian, Elizabethan, and Irish,* London 5411 12″. A great concert singer performs in a style that is far from folk, but still magnificent. Especially fine are "Over the Mountains," "My Boy Willie," "Keel Row," and "Blow the Wind Southerly."

FIELD TRIP—ENGLAND, collected and recorded by Jean Ritchie and George Pickow. Folkways distributes this Collector's Limited Edition CLE 1201, 12″. Some rare performances, picked up "on the spot," of such songs as "Widdecombe Fair," "Young Sailor Cut Down in His Prime," and "Oranges and Lemons."

GALVIN, PATRICK, *Irish Drinking Songs,* Riverside RLP 12-604 12″. Songs, mostly humorous, sung by a highly individual folk song scholar. Includes "The Cruiskeen Lawn," "Finnigan's Wake," and "The One-Eyed Riley."

GALVIN, PATRICK, *Irish Love Songs,* Riverside RLP 12-608 12″. One of the finest Irish folk song records. "Banks of the Roses," "The Wind That Shakes the Barley," "The Lark in the Clear Air," and a version of "Shule Aroon" that I have heard no other place.

GOODING, CYNTHIA, *Faithful Lovers and Other Phenomena,* Electra 107 12″. Immense verve and richness; particularly with "The Baliff's Daughter of Islington," "Lilliburlero," and "The Cherry-Tree Carol."

HAMMOND, DAVID, *I Am the Wee Falorie Man,* Tradition Records TLP 1028 12″. Songs from northern Ireland beautifully sung in traditional style. Notable are "Rockin' the Cradle," "'Tis Pretty to Be in Ballinderry," "'B' for Barney," and the children's song "Green Gravel." Mr. Hammond is surely the perfect singer for the songs on this admirable record.

HOUSE, WALLACE, *English Folk Songs,* Folkways FP 823 10″. A *tour de force,* sung in sixteen different dialects, all authentic-sounding. Particularly fine are "I'm Seventeen Cum Sunday," "On Ilkley Moor Bar T'at," "Old Farmer Buck," "Gently, Johnny, My Jingalo," and "The Eddystone Light."

IRELAND, The Columbia World Library of Folk and Primitive Music, collected and edited by Seamus Ennis and Alan Lomax, Columbia SL-204 12″. A must for every folk song collection; taped on-the-spot performances in Gaelic and English of thirty-four songs, instrumental and vocal.

IVES, BURL, *Songs of Ireland,* Decca DL 8444 12″. A fine selection of songs (although we *are* tired of "Molly Malone") including "Brennan on the Moor," "Kilgary Mountain," "Nell Flaherty's Drake," and "Mrs. McGrath."

LARK IN THE MORNING, THE, collected and edited by Diane Hamilton, Tradition TLP 1004 12″. Irish songs and dances, some performed by genuine "folk" folk singers, others by professionals. Notable are "Rockin' the Cradle," sung by Paddy Tunney, "The Wran Song," by Liam Clancy, and "The Little Beggarman," sung by Mrs. Sarah Makem and Tommy Makem.

LLOYD, A. A., *The Foggy Dew* and other traditional English love songs, Tradition TLP 1016 12″. Mr. Lloyd is so individual and so determined a folk song purist that he takes a little getting used to. But he's indeed worth it. Notable are "The Seven Gypsies," "The Husband with No Courage in Him," and "The Trees They Do Grow High."

MACCOLL, EWEN, assisted by Peggy Seeger, *Classic Scots Ballads,* Tradition TLP 1015 12″. One of the most satisfying records ever made. Mr. MacColl is the finest Scotch folk singer, and Miss Seeger joins him in many of the songs with the most fetching close harmony. Notable are "Johnny Lad," "The Maid Gaed to the Mill," "Mormond Braes," "The Trooper and the Maid," and "I Loved a Lass."

MACCOLL, EWAN, *Scots Drinking Songs,* Riverside RLP 12-605, 12″. Spirited, and not for children. Includes "We're a Jolly Fu'," "The Calton Weaver," "Green Grow the Rashes, O," and "The Wind Blew the Bonnie Lassie's Plaidie Awa'."

MACCOLL, EWAN, *Scots Folk Songs,* Riverside RLP 12-609, 12″. Includes "The Barnyards o' Delgatty," "Tail Toddle," and "Johnny Cope."

MACCOLL, EWAN and PEGGY SEEGER, SHUTTLE AND CAGE, Topic Records 10-T13 10″. Exciting industrial songs, including "The Wark o' the Weavers" and "Fourpence a Day."

MACCOLL, EWAN, *Songs of Two Rebellions,* The Jacobite Wars of 1715 and 1745 in Scotland, Folkways FW 8756 12″. The finest renditions possible of such great songs as "Such a Parcel of Rogues in a Nation," "Wae's Me for Prince Charlie," "The Bonnie Moorhen," and "Will Ye No' Come Back Again?"

MCCORMACK, JOHN, *A John McCormack Concert,* Avoca 33-AV-112 12″. As was customary with this great tenor, there is a lot of phony-Irish junk included, but the record *does* contain his moving "Oft in the Stilly Night."

MCEWEN, RORY and ALEX, *Scottish Songs and Ballads,* Folkways FW 930 10″. Two brothers in beautiful harmony. Especially fine are "Liezey Lindsey," "The Craw Killed the Pussie," and "Peerie Fairies" ("Baloo Baleary").

O'HARA, MARY, *Songs of Erin,* London LL 1572 12″. Great artistry; lovely songs. Includes "I Wish I Had the Shepherd's Lamb," "The Spanish Lady," "Eileen Aroon," and "The Spinning Wheel."

O'HARA, MARY, *Songs of Ireland,* Tradition TLP 1024 12". Purity and beauty from a great folk singer. About half the songs are in Gaelic. Notable are "Óro Mo Bhaidin" ("Óro My Little Boat"), "Maidrin Ruadh" ("The Little Red Fox"), "Dia Luain Dia Mairt" ("Monday, Tuesday") and "Farewell, but Whenever You Welcome the Hour."

RHOS MALE VOICE CHOIR, *Music from the Welsh Mines,* Washington WR-416 12". A rich, full choir sings hymns and folk songs. Especially fine are "Laudamus" ("Bryn Calfaria"), and "Myfanwy."

SCOTLAND, The Columbia World Library of Folk and Primitive Music, collected and edited by Alan Lomax, Columbia SL-209 12". A must for every folk song collection; includes the finest performance of "My Love is Like a Red Red Rose" I've ever heard, and Isla Cameron's singing of "O Can Ye Sew Cushions," among many other delights.

SUMMERS, ANDREW ROWAN, *The Lady Gay,* Folkways FA 2041 10". Includes "Early one Morning," "The Cherry Tree Carol," and "Old Bangum."

SUMMERS, ANDREW ROWAN, *Seeds of Love,* Folkways FP 21 10". This fine tenor sings the loveliest version of "Hares on the Mountain." Also noteworthy are "O No, John, No!" and "Blow Away the Dew."

THOMAS, THOMAS L., *Welsh Songs,* London 5172 12". A fine concert singer performs traditional songs in Welsh with harp accompaniment. All the songs are lovely. I especially recommend "Y Deryn Pur" ("The Dove"), "Dafydd Y Gareg Wen" ("David of the White Rock), and "Cyfri'r Giefr" ("Counting the Goats").

WALES, TONY, *Sussex Folk Songs and Ballads,* Folkways FG 3515 12". Delightful songs performed in an undeniably authentic manner by a young native. I especially enjoy "Peri-Iri-Igdum," "On Christmas Night," "Buttercup Joe," and "The Bailiff's Daughter of Islington."

WILLIAMS, GWILYM, *Welsh Songs,* Jay-3013 10". Eight of the best-known Welsh songs sung in Welsh by an actor and concert singer. "David of the White Rock" and "Land of My Fathers" (the national anthem) are particularly moving.

Index

TITLE INDEX

FIRST LINE INDEX